ATLANTIC ESCORTS

Hesperus, one of the most famous ships in the Atlantic battle, seen here in the Mersey. She was the leader of Captain Macintyre's B2 Escort Group. It was *Hesperus* which carried the body of the famous Captain 'Johnnie' Walker for burial at sea. Though her ensign appears to be at half mast in this photo, it was most probably taken in early 1945, a year later than the funeral.

ATLANTIC ESCORTS

Ships, Weapons & Tactics in World War II

David K Brown

Seaforth PUBLISHING

Copyright © David K Brown 2007

First published in Great Britain in 2007 by
Seaforth Publishing
An imprint of Pen & Sword Books Ltd
47 Church Street, Barnsley
S Yorkshire S70 2AS
Website: www.seaforthpublishing.com
Email: info@seaforthpublishing.com

Reprinted 2009

British Library Cataloguing in Publication Data
Brown, D K (David K)
Atlantic escorts : Ships, weapons and tactics in World War II
Warships - History - 20th century 2. Anti-submarine
warfare - History 3. World War, 1939-1945 - Campaigns - Atlantic Ocean
I. Title
623.8'254'09044

ISBN-13: 9781844157020

ISBN 978-1-84415-702-0

Designed and typeset by Mousemat Design Limited
Printed and bound in Thailand

Contents

Glossary

AA	anti-aircraft
ADNC(P)	Assistant Director of Naval Construction (Production)
AES	Admiralty Experimental Station (Parkeston Quay, Harwich), pioneer of asdic
AFO	Admiralty Fleet Order
AP	armour-piercing (of naval or artillery shells)
A/S	anti-submarine
ASI	Admiralty supply items
ASV	air-to-surface-vessel (of radar)
ASW	anti-submarine warfare
BL	breech-loading (of guns); in breech-loading, the shell was separate from the bagged charge (see QF)
CAFO	Confidential Admiralty Fleet Order
CNO	Chief of Naval Operations (US Navy post)
DMWD	Director of Miscellaneous Weapons Department
DNC	Director of Naval Construction
DNO	Director of Naval Ordnance
FAA	Fleet Air Arm
full period	in oscillatory motions such as roll, the period is the time from out to out, *and back*
GCCS	Government Code and Cipher School, Bletchley Park
GM	metacentric height, a measure of the stability of a ship
HA	high-angle (of guns)
HE	high-explosive
HF/DF	high-frequency direction finding
LSH(S)	Landing Ship Headquarters (Small)
MASB	motor anti-submarine boat
Mk 24 mine	US anti-submarine homing torpedo
mld	moulded to the inside of the hull plating; measurement of vessel's draught
oa	length overall
pp	length between perpendiculars
PPI	plan position indicator
QF	quick-firing (of guns); in quick-firers, the shell and brass cartridge were in one piece (see BL)
RCAF	Royal Canadian Air Force
RCN	Royal Canadian Navy
RDF	radio direction finding (the early cover name for radar)
TBS	inter-ship radio, sometimes interpreted as 'talk between ships'
vanishing angle of stability	the angle of heel at which the vessel will continue to roll over and capsize; it is a theoretical figure, since seawater is likely to have started to enter through the vessel's various ports and apertures before this angle is reached
WAIR	W class destroyers converted for anti-aircraft duty

Introduction

A W Watson, Assistant Director of Naval Construction, was responsible for most British escort design. The Director of Naval Construction, Sir Stanley Goodall, was to write in 1940, 'Watson is a really good man'.

The Battle of the Atlantic was the biggest battle of World War II, and yet little known to the public. It was big in geographical extent; from British harbours to North America on the convoy routes is some 3,000 miles, whilst the battle ranged from Greenland in the north to the Caribbean in the south. It was big in human tragedy; some 23,000 merchant seamen were lost, together with numerous RN, RCN and other naval personnel, air force crews of many nationalities and, on the Axis side, 27,000 U-boat crew. It was the longest battle of the war, with the first sinking taking place on 3 Sept 1939 and the last on 6 May 1945.

There have been fine general histories of the battle[1] but the subject is too vast for any one book. This volume will deal with escort vessels, their crews, sensors and weapon systems, together with the supporting systems that directed the battle, trained their crews and maintained their hardware. No tool is effective if the operator is unskilled and some crew members had never seen the sea before their first operational voyage.

Surface escort vessels sank 225 submarines, mainly in the earlier years of the war, when the RAF operated obsolescent aircraft that were of short range and equipped with ineffective weapons. From 1943 onwards these faults were overcome and, with ships and aircraft operating under common control, the RAF, RCAF and FAA came into their own, sinking 228 U-boats at sea. However, it is not unfair to say that the battle was largely won by the time that aircraft became effective.

This book only outlines the operational aspects of the battle itself, showing how problems in equipment, training and operational control were overcome. Reaction to a new threat was inevitably slow; it took fifteen to eighteen months to get a new class of ship from drawing bench to sea, and new weapons took even longer. Success depended more on anticipation than reaction time, though sometimes reaction was very swift; for example, the original aerial for the 268 radar was designed and built within a week.

A central theme is the inevitable conflict between the need for numbers and the capability of individual units – quality versus quantity – a balance in which the parameters changed with time. Under this heading we may mention the stupendous efforts in Canada in building and manning so many escorts.

The battle was won not by any single weapon or sensor but by the combined effects of many technologies used by well trained and co-ordinated crews, and by the lasting courage of the merchant men.

This book is intended as a tribute to the designers and builders of the escort vessels, as well as their operators, not forgetting the three commanders-in-chief.

A Note on Numbers

For many reasons, there is a lack of certainty about most of the numbers used in this story. For example, the figure of British merchant ship deaths in the battle is given above as 23,000. The total number of deaths in the merchant service was 34,000 but many were not due to U-boats, while others did not occur in the North Atlantic. This raises another problem: what are the geographical boundaries of the Battle of the Atlantic? I have excluded Arctic convoys and the east coast (North Sea), but where does the English Channel become the Atlantic – and should the South Atlantic be included?

In addition, I do not think that a long line of figures conveys much to the reader; 831,123 is more easily understood as 'about 830,000', though I will omit the 'about' unless it is of special significance.

Structure

The first seven chapters of the book are arranged chronologically, each chapter opening with a brief narrative of that phase of the battle. This is followed by a section on technical developments, mainly sensors and weapons, and then the significant ships joining during the period.

Maps

The maps reproduced here illustrating phases of the battle were first published in an official booklet, *The Battle of the Atlantic* (price one shilling! – now out of copyright). They show the positions in which U-boats and merchant ships were sunk. These positions were based on wartime information; post-war research has shown them to contain a few errors but they still give a vivid impression of the geographical shifts in the battle. The chronological divisions of the phases shown on the maps differ slightly from those used as chapter headings, but a month or so makes little difference to the picture.

The maps are drawn using Mercator's projection, which uses an increasing scale as the latitude gets more northerly, so that a convoy route appears to be far from being a great circle. The sketch map reproduced left is based on a gnomonic projection, which shows a great circle route as a straight line. It will be seen that the typical convoy track departs only slightly from a great circle.

Acknowledgements

Ian Buxton, Rob Gardiner, Cdre (now Rear Adm) James Goldrick RAN, John Lambert, George Moore, John Roberts and Phil Sims.

This sketch map is based on a gnomic projection which shows a 'Great Circle' route as a straight line avoiding the distortion of a Mercator's projection at high latitudes. The typical convoy route deviates only slightly from the Great Circle to bring it within air cover from Iceland and provide some degree of evasion.

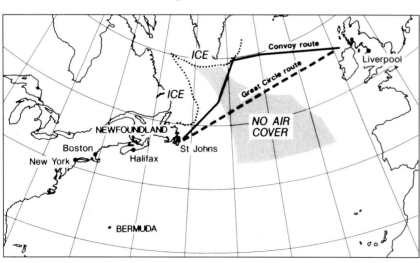

1 Between the Wars

The Lessons of World War I

There does not seem to have been any high level discussion paper on the lessons of the submarine war of 1914–18. In part, this may have been a result of excessive secrecy, particularly with regard to intelligence, direction-finding, etc.[1] The notes that follow are based on hindsight.

The first lesson was that the UK was very close to defeat in 1917 and remained vulnerable to submarine attack. The German U-boat force had three main objectives: to weaken the Grand Fleet by attrition, so that the High Seas Fleet could fight on level terms; to defeat the UK by starvation; and to prevent the US Army from reaching France.[2]

The U-boats failed in all three. Attempts to attack the Grand Fleet and US army transports had negligible results. At the end of 1916 a German report estimated that sinking 600,000 tons of merchant shipping per month would bring victory within five months. The losses in 1917 were terrible but monthly sinkings only twice exceeded 600,000 tons. Attacks on merchant shipping came close to success but were defeated mainly by the introduction of convoy. Even so, large numbers of escorts were needed. 'Hunting' without precise location was of no value.

The enormous building programme of merchant ships (and escorts) in the USA was a major contributory factor. This was only partially offset by the building of U-boats, which by 1918 had steadied at about eight boats per month. There were concerted efforts to increase the building rate, but with little success. It is probable that the bottleneck lay in the supply of auxiliaries such as pumps, periscopes, etc., whilst training of crews – commanding officers in

Cachalot, a World War I escort based on a whale catcher. She was used in numerous trials of early asdic development.

particular – remained a problem. However, defence analysts in the late thirties would have been wise to expect Germany to achieve at least an equal rate of completion of submarines.

Tactically, the increasing number of night, surface attacks in 1918 should have been noted, though these were solo attacks and not the wolf pack attacks of the later war. It should also have been recognised that even in 1917 U-boats could reach the east coast of the USA from German bases. The lengthy building time for U-cruisers, together with their relative lack of success, was misread and most big navies began to build 'monster' submarines.[3]

After the war there seems to have been a comfortable feeling that submarines had been defeated without the use of asdic, while whispers of this new sensor suggested that submarines had lost their cloak of invisibility. There were attempts to agree an international ban on submarines but they were never likely to succeed. Indeed, the RN submarine-building programme for the Far East suggests that it was recognised that a ban was never likely to be agreed. There was agreement that any submarine attacking a merchant ship would obey Prize Rules on safety of the crew, etc. but it is likely that there was little confidence that this would be maintained.

The Threat
In the 1920s there was little or no submarine threat to British merchant shipping. The USA had been ruled out as a potential enemy in the early years of the century and though the build up of French bombers and submarines was a matter of concern, the Entente Cordiale still held. Japan was seen as a potential enemy and was building a considerable number of fleet submarines but it was believed (correctly) that Japanese doctrine saw these boats as of use against an enemy battle fleet rather than merchant shipping.

Under the Versailles Treaty, Germany was forbidden to build or own submarines. However, as early as 1922, a design bureau, N V Ingenieurskantoor voor Scheepsbouw (IvS), was set up at The Hague to preserve German expertise by designing submarines for other nations. In 1926 they received an order for two

boats from Turkey and trials were carried out in 1928 with German personnel. Also in 1928 an order for three boats was received from Finland. These went on trials in 1930, again with German crews. In 1934 another Finnish boat, *Vessiko*, the prototype of the later Type IIA of the German Navy, went on trials with a mixed Finnish and German crew. Later she was used to train German submarine crews. The Admiralty was aware of these developments[4] but saw them as not a serious threat and even, perhaps, a bulwark against the Soviet Union.

On coming to power, Hitler's Nazi Party renounced the treaty restrictions of Versailles and began to produce material for a submarine fleet. Construction of the Type IA began in 1935; this type was based on a boat ordered by Spain as E1 but sold to Turkey before completion. The Type IA seems to have been unsuccessful, as only two were built. They were followed by the 250-ton Type IIA, which completed only four months after they were laid down, as so much preparatory work had been done. Their main function was crew training but the British Admiralty saw them as designed for Baltic operations against the Soviet Union.

The Anglo-German Treaty of December 1935 limited the tonnage of the German submarine fleet to 45 per cent of that of the RN but with an escalator clause permitting an increase to equality in the event of a threat from a third party, after discussion. This clause was invoked in December 1938 without discussion.

Budgets
During the 1920s and early 30s, expenditure on the Navy was very tight. Battleship-building was forbidden under the Washington Treaty, extended by the London Treaty to 1937, but available building funds went mainly on cruisers and destroyers. A very few sloops were built as prototype minesweepers and escorts that could be used in peacetime as colonial policemen. It should be remembered that the Army and the RAF were, if anything, even worse funded than the Navy.[5]

The development of asdic, discussed later, gave priority to research and prototype units rather than an early production fit. Improvements

Torrid was used for trials of an ahead-throwing A/S weapon in the early 1930s. Mounted in A-position, it fired a stick bomb up to 800 yards. Target location with the asdics of the day was not good enough and effort was not available to cure the problems.

followed each other rapidly and with no serious threat this may be seen as a wise policy. It did result in the A class destroyers and a few sloops completing 'for, but not with, asdic', although this was remedied before the war. Some effort was put into the development of an ahead-throwing weapon (see photo of *Torrid*) but this was abandoned because asdic technology was not then accurate enough to direct such a weapon without major work. Resources were scarce and needed for work seen as higher priority.

Tactics and Training

The flotilla at Portland developed the tactical use of asdic and in so doing exposed most of its weaknesses. In particular, the bending of the asdic beam by layers of water of different density was known, mainly from trials in the Mediterranean, though the full effect was probably not appreciated until the Spanish Civil War and the Neutrality patrols.

Exercises with submerged submarines were not, with rare exceptions, permitted after dark, though a few night exercises took place using surfaced submarines – surely more dangerous? Hence the value of night surface attack by submarines was known to some extent.[6] There was a lack of awareness of the extent to which night surface attack was employed in the last year of World War I. Detection of a low-lying submarine by eye on a dark night is very

difficult, a problem only solved when effective radar sets became available. Overall, those involved in ASW had developed effective weapon systems controlled by asdic, and tactics to employ these systems. However, as Franklin has shown, ASW officers did not figure in the higher ranks of the Admiralty, who were not fully aware of either the capability of ASW forces or their limitations.

Early 1930s

A major review of ASW was carried out in 1932,[7] when there was still no direct submarine threat to the UK. The potential threat was already seen as Germany, even though she had no submarines at that date and it was envisaged that the lengthy voyage round the north of Scotland would mean few U-boats on station. These few could be countered by the older destroyers of the A–I classes and earlier destroyers, and by the few sloops. It was recognised that minesweeping and ASW had differing requirements, particularly as to draught, and the convoy sloop departed from the minesweeper design. It is, perhaps, ironic that the *Halcyon* class minesweeping sloops spent much of the war as ASW ships. The east coast was seen as the danger area and a number of countermeasures were put in hand. That area of operations lies outside the scope of this book but we shall look at it briefly for the sake of completeness.

The aircraft threat was recognised as serious on the east coast and led to the Hunt class with a very heavy AA armament; a number of older V&W class destroyers were also modernised with a heavy AA armament. A new design of coastal sloop was designed to provide A/S protection. They were beautiful little ships but far too expensive to be built in numbers. Their draught was too small for optimum asdic performance, a fault made worse in the first six, where the weight calculations were in error and they floated nearly a foot lighter than the inadequate design figure.[8]

Much of the coastal escort force would be made up of trawlers, and a prototype conversion of a commercial-style trawler was fitted out. The ship chosen was the *James Ludford*, built for the Royal Navy in World War I but typical of older commercial trawlers. Her conversion was judged successful and formed the model for many more during the war. In addition, *Basset*, a prototype of a new-design ship on trawler style, was built. She, too, was successful and some 200 generally similar ships of the Isle and Dance classes were built during the war. It was recognised even before the war that trawlers were on the small side for A/S ships and a larger vessel was developed from a whale catcher. These ships entered service as the Flower class corvettes, discussed in the next chapter.

Convoy Organisation[9]

During the 1930s it was Admiralty policy that convoy would be introduced only when the enemy resorted to unrestricted warfare and losses of merchant ships became unsupportable. This doctrine was carried to extreme in earlier years, exemplified by a speech in a debate in Parliament in 1935 by Lord Stanley (Parliamentary Secretary) in which he trotted out all the old objections that had been shown to be insignificant in World War I – waste of time in assembly, reduction to the pace of the slowest, port congestion, etc.

However, in January 1937 a Shipping Defence Advisory Committee (SDAC) was set up, at the suggestion of Adm James.[10] The committee was to bring together the numerous bodies involved from ministries, the navy, ship owners and technical experts. There were seven subcommittees on specific topics, such as strengthening decks for defensive armament (and arranging payment), communication between bridge and engine room, assembly ports, convoy organisation (including commodores), provision of secret code books, war risk insurance and handbooks.

The subcommittees reported to the main body in July 1937, when Adm James made clear the Admiralty policy 'that the convoy system is considered by the Admiralty to be the most effective form of protection against surface,

Picotee. She is typical of the early Flower class, which were the only escorts which could be built in numbers in 1939. She mounts a four-barrelled machine gun in place of her pom-pom. (WSS)

submarine or air attack'. In the July meeting, James assured them that convoy would be introduced as soon as there was a significant threat, and that there were sufficient escort vessels.

The vice-chairman was Paymaster Rear Adm Sir Eldon Manisty, who, as a commander, had been involved in convoy organisation during World War I. He was a tower of strength and undertook a worldwide tour in 1938 to visit and inspect assembly ports and their local organisation. He outlined to each commander-in-chief and the local naval control officer the organisation that would be needed and helped to find the staff required. From 1935 Adm Manisty had developed a new Trade Division within the Admiralty, together with a Naval Control Service to direct shipping. Many of these posts were filled by retired naval officers.

The organisation was tested in the 1938 Munich crisis and a very few loose ends tied up before the war. The sinking of the *Athenia* on 3 September was taken, probably incorrectly, as the start of unrestricted warfare and the convoy organisation set in motion. It worked well and there were few omissions.

Asdic Development between the Wars[11]

During 1916 a small team of scientists at the Admiralty Experimental Station (AES), Parkeston Quay began to study the use of echo ranging with high-frequency sound.[12] The principle was simple: a transducer would send out a short pulse of high-frequency sound which would be reflected from a submarine or any other object in its path. The reflected sound would be picked up by the same transducer and the time from sending to reception would give the distance to the target, if the speed of sound in water were known, while the bearing was given by the direction in which the transducer was pointing. Though the principle was simple, implementation was far from easy; every phrase in the preceding sentences conceals difficult, practical problems.

By 1918 it had been found that quartz was the most suitable material for the transducers and these were cut by a firm of tombstone makers, with the help of the Geological Survey Museum. It was all very secret, though there were some useful exchanges with the French, who were working on similar lines.[13]

It was soon found that the transducers worked best if enclosed in a dome, which prevented noise from the water flow over the face from interfering with the signal. Initial trials in the summer of 1918 were carried out first in a barge on the River Stour and then under the drifter *Hiedra*. In October 1918 a prototype set was tried in the trawler *Ebro II*, which got good echoes at 600 yards. As a result a first batch of twenty production sets was ordered and fitting drawings prepared for several classes of escorts. The patrol vessel P59 and the whaler *Cachalot* were fitted. By early 1919, echo ranges of 1,100 yards were obtained under ideal conditions and a set fitted in P55 was developed into the first production set, Type 112, which had a fifteen-inch transducer housed in a retractable, cylindrical, canvas dome, permitting operation up to twenty knots. Detection ranges of 2,500–3,000 yards were obtained. Ship-fitting of the 112 set began in 1920 with the 1st A/S Flotilla at Portland – mainly P and PC boats with a couple of whalers.

Once the war was over, the pace slowed down and further delay was caused by a sensible rationalisation of research establishments. In post-war years the initial emphasis was on basic research. This was a wise decision as basic knowledge of the sea, of transducers and supporting technology was minimal, whilst each new design of set was an improvement on earlier ones. Setting this continual development against the lack of any real threat and the small navy

Other early asdic trials were carried out with P boats similar to *P40*. (WSS)

votes, it was obvious that a large production plan would be unwise.

One of the first tasks in 1920–2 was an accurate determination of the speed of sound in water (about 1,510m/s, depending on density and salinity). There was an important trial in 1922, when the *Rocket* and the submarine H32 went into the Red Sea, Mediterranean, Marmara and the Black Sea to explore the effect of sea water temperature; the cement fixing the quartz to the backing plate failed. This trial also showed that the asdic beam could be bent by sea water layers of different density, a problem further explored in 1930 by P59 and H32 with a new Type 119 set.

Bending of the beam by density layers was only one of the problems of early sets. The beam could be reflected by objects other than submarines – 'non-subs' as they were known – such as shoals of fish, wrecks, rocks and even tide rips. Much depended on the 'ear' of the operator, though the introduction of the range recorder enabled him to see whether the object was moving. These sets gave range and bearing but only a slight indication of depth, determined from the range at which the target entered and left the conical sound beam. The significance of the lack of depth indication was not fully appreciated, as many of the trials and exercises were conducted near Portland where the sea was fairly shallow.

Sea trials in the 1920s showed that asdic sets could be used in passive mode to listen for the enemy. A submarine could detect a destroyer steaming at fifteen knots at 1,000 yards. Work on surface passive sets was stopped to make more effort available for active sets, though some effort was put into submarine sets and into making British submarines quieter in the light of known German interest in listening equipment. Similar trials showed that noise picked up by the asdic included noise from flow over the dome and cavitation on the propellers.

The original transducer (Type 112) consisted of a single layer of quartz sandwiched between two steel plates. By 1928 the transducer was a two-ply sandwich, and in 1935 a four-ply was introduced, which remained standard until after

By 1939 all the inter-war destroyers of the A-I classes had been fitted with asdic. *Foxhound* in 1942 had changed little. A 3in AA gun has replaced one set of torpedo tubes and Y gun has been removed. She has an early radar at the remaining masthead.

the war. Most were cut by a small firm of masons at Portland.

Dome design presented problems. Until 1928 DNC would not allow the keel to be cut. Even when this was relaxed DNC would only agree to cut-outs of less than two frame spaces, say fifty-five inches. This was not conservatism, but recognition that existing structural design methods could not cope with breaks in the main structural member in the highly loaded slamming area. The height of the dome was limited to fifty-four inches by the height of the dock blocks. Many trials evaluated different domes and their position, some even with a human observer inside the dome. Materials were another problem; early domes of Duralumin lasted a few months only, before corroding away. By about 1930 a satisfactory fifty-four-inch dome was designed for the first 'production' fit in the B class destroyers, which raised operating speeds to twenty-five knots.

The earliest sets required the time for the sound pulse to travel to the target and back to be measured with a stopwatch and, indeed, a stopwatch was retained as a back-up throughout the war. The introduction of a recorder that would not only give the range but make a permanent record of where the echo had moved was a major advance. The development was headed by the echo sounder team, where funding was slightly less difficult. Lack of an accurate recorder was given as the main reason for abandoning the ahead-throwing weapon in the early 1930s. By about 1932 a recorder using sensitised paper and a very accurate drive motor had been produced; for the first time asdic had a memory, from which target speed could be deduced. This marked the coming of age of A/S weapon 'systems', as opposed to a collection of independent widgets, and the situation was further improved by an increasing number of training aids.

By the end of the 1920s it seems to have been agreed that all new destroyers should be designed for asdic but only alternate flotillas would be fitted. In 1924 the 6th Destroyer Flotilla of V&Ws (and the leader, *Campbell*) was fitted with Type 112. The design of a production set was not ready for the A class, so the B class was the first flotilla to be equipped (Type 119). The curtailed C class of four ships were not fitted during build but were equipped soon after. Later flotillas all seem to have been fitted on build. Type 119 became the standard pre-war destroyer set and was frequently updated. After *Hunter* was mined in 1937, a short-pulse mine detection attachment was developed. The D class had Type 121, with similar electronics to 119 but a gyro-stabilised transducer. It could operate to twenty-four knots and was also fitted in sloops from *Bittern* onwards. A further-development 124 appeared in 1924, which incorporated the range recorder and an improved amplifier. By 1937 it was being installed in those older destroyers that did not already have asdic.

By the early 1930s it was already clear that the numbers of A/S vessels would always be inadequate and consideration was give to the use of fishing trawlers. Two sets were developed: Type 122 for ships with a turbo alternator, and Type 123 for those with an HF motor alternator. Both had portable domes. For these slow ships, retractable domes were not needed.

By the spring of 1939 the Admiralty had brought the Operational Intelligence Room, the Surface Ship Plot and the Submarine Tracking Room to full readiness. By the outbreak of war, there were some 200 ships fitted with asdic, including 100 of the more modern destroyers, 45 sloops and older destroyers and 20 A/S trawlers. In addition there were a further 200 sets stockpiled for requisitioned trawlers.[14] Quartz had to be imported and a stock pile was built up, with purchases of one to three hundredweight each year from 1935.

Admiralty R and S Classes[15]

These two classes saw the introduction of geared turbines to the standard World War I destroyer, entering service from 1917 onwards. Comparative trials between *Romola* and the ungeared *Norman* showed fuel savings of 15 per cent at eighteen knots and 28 per cent at twenty-five knots, which, combined with an increase in fuel stowage, gave a useful increase in endurance, quoted as 3,440 miles at fifteen knots in the R class and very slightly more in the S class. As built, they had a trial speed of about thirty-six

Skate was the only survivor of the World War I R class destroyer. This model by Julian Glossop shows her late in the second war, with a radar tower aft and ten-pattern depth charge fit.

knots and carried three 4in guns and four 21in torpedo tubes. By 1939 there were one surviving R class (*Skate*) and eleven S class.

Table 1.1: R and S classes

Displacement (tons):	905 (*Skate* 900), 1,220 full load
Dimensions (feet):	265 pp, 276 oa x 26¾ x 8½/10¾
Shp and speed (kts):	27,000 = 36 (32½ full load)
Fuel (tons), endurance (miles) @ (kts):	3,440 @ 15
Complement:	90

Table 1.1 shows the technical details of the R and S classes. Note that in this and other tables the figure for endurance is nominal. Though it is based on actual trials figures, the real endurance in war was much less. All boilers were kept on line most of the time and high speed was used quite often; consumption by auxiliary plant was much higher. While the endurance figures quoted should not be regarded as accurately reflecting performance in operation, they were measured in the same way for all classes and provide a basis for drawing comparisons between them.

The S class was the ultimate development of the standard destroyer of World War I. The two forward boiler uptakes were trunked into a single funnel, which enabled the bridge to be moved aft and thus reduced the perceived motions. The sheer was increased and the stem slightly raked. For their day they were seen as good sea boats though soon overshadowed by the V&Ws. During the thirties several were modified for special tasks and as minelayers, while other changes were made for Operation Catherine.[16]

Below and above right: Two views of *Scimitar*: the one with white pendant numbers dates from 1940 and shows the beauty of these fast but fragile ships. The other picture is about a year later and the machine guns have been replaced by 20mm Oerlikons. The quarterdeck is congested with fourteen-pattern depth charge fittings.

Perhaps surprisingly, those in Western Approaches soon reached a fairly uniform style.

These units had a single 4in in A-position and a 12pdr HA amidships. Initially, they had the heavy fourteen-pattern depth charge outfit (eight throwers and two rails) but this was reduced to ten-pattern in most, with only four throwers. They had Type 133 asdic and 286 radar, replaced in most by 291, though *Skate* and *Shikari* had 271 on a short lattice mast aft. Their elderly engines could still drive them at over thirty knots on a calm day, and these beautiful ships made a fine sight at speed.[17] They had more power for their size than any other Western Approaches ship and were a delight to handle.

However, they had never been intended to be driven hard in rough weather and damage was frequent. Some lost a funnel; boats were so frequently lost that they were no longer issued with motor boats. The bridge front was often damaged; one captain was killed in his bunk in the sea cabin. Reluctantly they were soon paid off or used for training. The Admiralty is often criticised for scrapping ships between the wars that would have been valuable in the war to come – ninety-seven ships of the R and S classes were scrapped. But did we really want to spare crews and maintenance facilities for ships like these?

Older Destroyers (V&W, Leaders)[18]

The V&W classes, with their leaders, were the finest destroyers of World War I. Others may

Veteran has full ASW equipment but did not receive a long-range conversion. She retains the forward torpedo tubes. (IWM A 7562)

have been more heavily armed or faster but the V&Ws seem to have achieved the best balance of military qualities. Their design by C D Hannaford shows how rearrangement of conventional features can lead to a step change in capability. The introduction of the R class with a sea speed of thirty-four knots showed the need for a faster leader. A number of sketch designs were considered but the solution was to copy the superimposed guns forward from the *Seymour* class and use a similar arrangement aft. The new 4in Mk V quick-firer (QF) was fitted and, even allowing for the longer barrel, the ship could be a little shorter at 312 feet overall. A fifth 4in was considered but replaced by a 3in HA gun. The geared-turbine plant of the R class was adopted but the two forward funnels were combined so that the bridge could be a little further aft to make it dryer. Moving the bridge and the forward guns aft reduced the vertical accelerations perceived at those positions, adding to their reputation as good sea boats. Five V leaders were ordered, completing in mid-1917.

Following Jutland there was a demand for more heavily armed destroyers and, after various possibilities were considered, it was decided to order twenty-one very slightly modified V class in July 1917. Four more followed the next month. Even more speed was wanted but speed is expensive and nineteen 'repeats' were ordered in December 1916, together with two modified ships from Thornycroft. However, proponents of gunpower won out and the sixteen ships (plus two Thornycroft specials) of the modified W class ordered in January 1918 were a knot slower but carried four 4.7in guns (nine were cancelled when the war ended). This gun was a breech-loader with a slower rate of fire but a 50lb shell instead of the 35lb of the 4in. The last nine ships had the long boiler room adjacent to the engine room, seriously reducing their ability to survive underwater damage amidships. The consequent rearrangement meant that the fore funnel was the thicker one and, more important, A and B guns moved a little further aft. In April 1918, thirty-eight of these modified ships were ordered (twenty-nine cancelled).

Table 1.2: V class (W slightly heavier)	
Displacement (tons): 1,090, 1,480 full load	
Dimensions (feet): 300 pp, 312 oa x 29½ x 8½/11¾	
Shp and speed (kts): 27,000 = 34 (32 full load)	
Fuel (tons), endurance (miles) @ (kts): 367, 3,500 @ 15	
Complement: 134	

The Thornycroft specials were bigger (1,120/1,512 tons), faster (thirty-five knots) and more expensive than the Admiralty-design ships. This was mainly due to more powerful machinery but they ran trials on the St Catherine's mile, where the effect of shallow water gave them a bonus of one and a half knots. This was not 'cheating'; the benefit was well known both to Thornycroft and the Admiralty. They had the real advantage of greater freeboard.

Post-war destroyers did not enter service until the thirties, so for a decade the V&W class were indisputably the best. Even in the thirties the new destroyers of the A–I classes were of only slightly greater capability than the V&Ws, and the older classes were said to be more robust.

By 1939, twelve of these ships were gone – three sunk in World War I or its aftermath in the Baltic, one (*Bruce*) in trials of a torpedo with magnetic actuation, and the rest scrapped. *Valhalla* went in 1931, known to need an expensive refit. The four that were scrapped later had spent eleven to fifteen years in reserve, more damaging than the wear and tear of active service. *Walrus* ran aground whilst being towed to a WAIR refit.

Most of the rest had had a fairly eventful life between the wars. Though there was some wear and tear, this active life did ensure that they were well maintained. Most had been built with galvanised plating and framing.[19] Galvanising seemed expensive and time-consuming during World War I but it paid off during the later war. Few changes had been made; twin torpedo tubes were replaced with triples (five exceptions) and asdic Type 121 (or later variants) was fitted. Very little had been done to improve living conditions, with mess decks poorly insulated and inadequately heated. The coal-fired galleys were

Malcolm, a leader, had much the same fit as Veteran.

obsolete. Hard-lying money was reintroduced during the winter months as partial compensation. The inter-war complement of 110–15 rose to 170 during the war

A total of fifteen (plus *Wallace*) were converted to 'WAIRS' with a heavy AA armament of two twin 4in and two four-barrel machine guns. They were used almost exclusively on the east coast and played no part in the Battle of the Atlantic. Some thirty-eight of the remainder were available for Western Approaches work or preparing for such duties. Many had been in reserve until very recently and their crews had a high proportion of reservists, who took a little while to get back to efficiency. The Review of the Reserve Fleet at Weymouth just before the war helped to bring the crews up to standard.

Early changes were few; some vessels had a 12pdr HA in place of a set of torpedo tubes, Oerlikons were fitted when available and, later, radar was installed. AFOs in 1940 and 1941 approved the fitting of electric heaters and the installation of lagging and lining in mess decks but this work had low priority and was only carried out when the ship was in hand for a refit. As so often with lightly built, riveted ships, there were leaks in the forecastle deck into mess decks and through the shell into fuel and reserve feed tanks. Despite their age, the V&Ws seem to have been little worse than later destroyers. As

Atlantic escorts, their main problem was lack of endurance, quoted at 2,180 miles at fourteen knots with some 370 tons of oil. Like all destroyers of both world wars, the low freeboard abaft the forecastle made fore and aft access very dangerous in bad weather. Only in the last Emergency classes were flying bridges installed above the torpedo tubes, making access merely uncomfortable.

Long Range Escorts

The V&Ws had three boilers, the majority of the ships having one boiler in the forward boiler room and two in the longer room adjacent to the engine room. Starting with *Vimy* in January 1941, the forward boiler was removed and the lower part of the boiler room converted into fuel tanks, increasing endurance to 2,780 miles at fourteen knots with 450 tons of fuel. The upper layer became an additional mess deck, sorely needed in these overcrowded ships. The complement had gone up to 160–70. The loss of a boiler reduced power to 18,000shp and speed to 24½ knots.

B and X guns (4in or 4.7in) were retained and A gun was replaced by Hedgehog. In some early conversions, Hedgehog was not available and A gun was retained briefly (*Vimy*, *Vansittart*).[20] Some retained one triple torpedo mounting for launching heavy Mk 10 depth

Vimy has had a long-range conversion but, unusually, retains A gun, presumably because her Hedgehog mount was not ready.

By August 1942 *Whitehall* had lost the experimental five-mortar fitting (See Chapter 7) and was a conventional Long Range Escort (LRE). She seems to have a ten-pattern depth charge fit.

Vidette is another standard LRE. (IWM HU 1445)

The big after funnel marks *Viscount* as a Thornycroft Special but otherwise is a standard LRE. (IWM A 10712)

charges. Initially they retained the 12pdr but this was generally removed to make way for more depth charges. Four or five Oerlikons were added. Radar types 271 and 291 were fitted and roughly half had HF/DF with asdic 144. Up to 150 depth charges were carried.

In all, twenty ships were converted, eleven in the dockyards and nine in commercial yards, the work typically taking about six months, though there were considerable variations depending on

the defect list and on other work in hand.[21] An improved long-range escort (LRE) version was considered in January 1943.[22] It had 4in guns in A and X positions, a Hedgehog behind A, a twin torpedo tube, and two twin and two single Oerlikons. There was a new bridge (not sketched) with a lattice mast. Another study was for a tanker version. All old machinery was removed and twin diesels gave a speed of fifteen to seventeen knots. She would have carried 711

Keppel (and her sister *Broke*) were the only two-funnelled LREs. Originally she had three boiler rooms and lost the forward one in conversion but still needed two funnels. (IWM A15039)

tons of fuel and 200 depth charges for transfer. The guns and funnel were dummies.

Keppel, a Thornycroft leader, was an interesting variant on the LRE theme. As built, she had four boilers in three boiler rooms (1:2:1), the uptakes trunked into two large, flat-sided funnels, and carried a total of 500 tons of oil (398 main, 102 peace tanks[23]). On conversion, the forward boiler was removed and the lower part of the space converted to an 80-ton fuel tank, bringing her total capacity to 580 tons. This gave her an endurance of 5,700 tons at fifteen knots and a top speed (estimated) of twenty-five and a half knots, at which the endurance was 860 miles. A photo[24] shows her with a slender forward funnel. She is mounting two 4.7in, one 12pdr and three Oerlikons, together with Hedgehog, four depth charge throwers, two rails and two triple torpedo tubes. Later, in April 1944, she lost the tubes and probably the 12pdr and carried 140 depth charges. It is probable that *Broke* was similarly modified.

Major conversions of elderly tubs are rarely worthwhile but the Long Range Escorts seem to be an exception. They were still faster than most escorts and had the most modern A/S armament. The long-range conversion worked well because the original armament was on the upper deck and the removal of half the guns and the tubes helped to retain satisfactory stability.

Early Sloops

During World War I a large number of Flower class sloops were built. Originally, their primary role was seen as minesweeping but increasingly they became used as escorts. An original requirement to carry up to 1,000 men, operating as a ferry, proved valuable since, without these men, there was a considerable stability margin. In post-war years a number of these ships were used as colonial policemen, but by the mid- to late 1920s they were wearing out.

Considerable thought was given to their replacements and it was originally intended to build two prototypes, one with steam turbine machinery and the other with diesel engines, but no suitable UK engines could be found.[25] Their wartime role was again primarily minesweeping,

Wallflower was a typical World War I sloop, a type intended for minesweeping but mainly used as escorts.

Wellington in 1935 with a quarterdeck full of minesweeping gear and not an A/S weapon in sight. *Wellington* is still (2007) afloat on the Thames as a club house but little more than the bare hull remains.

for which a shallow draught was seen as desirable (8 feet 6 inches was chosen). Later this shallow draught was seen as a handicap for asdic operation. Anti-submarine warfare was not neglected; it seems always to have been envisaged that they would have asdic. However, sets were not available and the early classes were completed without. By the outbreak of war they had been fitted with Type 127, replaced when Hedgehog was fitted by Type 144. Four depth charge chutes were held on board, disassembled; many chutes and rails were held in store after being removed when ships were disposed of after the first war. Two depth charge throwers were

Left: Bridgewater was the first post-war design with many features of the earlier ships – including the big openings in the side which had to be closed to improve stability at large angles of heel. (John Roberts)

Right: By 1943 *Bridgewater* had a full ASW fit with at least two radars and HF/DF.

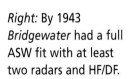

held in their home dockyard, as were the depth charges, many also dating back to the war.

The armament was intended to include two single 4in on HA (high-angle) mounts but, to save money, one was replaced by an LA (low-angle) mount from store. The LA gun was replaced in 1938 by an HA mount when the ships also received a quadruple 0.5in machine gun. It was intended that the second gun should be an alternative to the minesweeping winch, but they completed with both and the complement rose from seventy-six to ninety-six. Partly as a result of this weight growth, the stability of the first ships was poor, particularly at large angles of heel (vanishing angle 57°). They had been designed with a short, watertight forecastle though the deck itself continued well aft above openings in the side.[26] The large-angle stability was greatly improved by making the side watertight to the forecastle deck and by the addition of thirty tons of ballast. This simple stability problem suggests that their design was not taken seriously enough. The fact that there was no launching ceremony for the first four ships may be seen as a further example of their lowly status.

The 1927 Estimates brought orders for two ships, of the *Bridgewater* class (table 1.3). These two were followed by several very similar classes: four *Hastings*, four *Shoreham*, four *Falmouth*. The eight ships of the *Grimsby* class introduced changes in gun armament. Most had two 4.7in LA and one 3in HA. *Aberdeen* had a reduced armament of two 4in HA as a C-in-C's yacht, while *Fleetwood* had two twin 4in HA (it seems likely that this was the intended armament of the whole class). The additional AA gun fit was of little value without fire control. According to Rowland Baker, the *Grimsby* was the first sloop with correct weight calculations.

Table 1.3: *Bridgewater* class
Displacement (tons): 1,045, 1,360 deep
Dimensions (feet): 266¼ x 34 x 8¾/11½
Shp and speed (kts): 2,000 = 16.5
Fuel (tons), endurance (miles) @ (kts): 282, 4,500 @ 10
Complement: 95

Table 1.4: *Grimsby* class
Displacement (tons): 990, 1,300 deep
Dimensions (feet): 265 x 34 x 7¼
Shp and speed (kts): 2,000 = 16.5
Fuel (tons), endurance (miles) @ (kts): 300, 5,700 @ 10
Complement: 100

Mallard was designed as a small A/S escort for east coast work. They were too expensive to build in numbers.

Table 1.5: Sloop orders, 1927–34		
Programme	Ships	Notes
1927	2 *Bridgewater*	
1928	4 *Hastings*	+ RIN *Hindustan*
1929	4 *Shoreham*	
1930	4 *Falmouth*	
1931	2 *Grimsby*	+ *Halcyon* class minesweeping sloops
1932	2 *Grimsby*	
1933	2 repeat *Grimsby*	+ RIN *Indus* and *Kingfisher* coastal sloops
1934	2 repeat *Grimsby*	+ 4 RAN

By 1931 it was obvious that the combined minesweeper/escort role was not appropriate and a new class of small minesweeping sloops, the *Halcyon*s, was introduced. Ironically, most of them spent much of the war on A/S escort duties in the Arctic.

Wartime changes varied but the following is typical. They were fitted with a second quadruple machine gun in 1939. The machine guns were replaced by single Oerlikons in spring 1942 and two more (for a total of four) added in 1943 when Hedgehog was fitted[27] and asdic 144 installed. Radar 268 was fitted in 1941, replaced by 271 in 1942, and modified to 271Q in 1943, when some received 291 as well. HF/DF was fitted to most in 1942–3. The depth charge outfit was increased to forty at the outbreak of war.

The considerable number of fairly similar ships built over eight years shows that the naval staff were well satisfied. A consultation exercise in 1930 seemed to express satisfaction, though asking for heavier armament and an aircraft, both seen as impossible within the financial limits.[28] They were reasonable sea boats, with bilge keels sixteen inches deep (fairly high for the era) to reduce rolling, and sufficient length to limit pitch.

The Washington Treaty imposed no limits on smaller ships. The London Treaty (1930) placed no restriction on ships under 2,000 tons, a speed of

Hawthorn was typical of many commercial trawlers converted for ASW. They were too small to carry a full range of ASW equipments and their operators.

less than twenty knots and an armament of no more than four 6.1in guns and no torpedoes. There were no limits on vessels of less than 600 tons.

The emphasis placed on escorts for coastal convoys in the early 1930s led to the design of the six coastal sloops of the *Kingfisher* class in 1934 (later reclassified as patrol vessels and later still as corvettes). They were designed to come under the 600-ton barrier of the London Treaty and looked like a toy destroyer. This emphasis on weight-saving was unfortunate as the design draught was on the low side for good asdic operation and they completed very light, with one foot less draught. At £160,000 and with turbine machinery they were far too expensive for mass production. Three modified ships of the *Guillemot* class were built under the 1937 Estimates. They had heavier scantlings to increase draught. None of these pretty little ships played any part in the Battle of the Atlantic, though they did good work on the east coast, which was what they had been designed for.

The older sloops participated in twelve U-boat sinkings. Note that turbine machinery made them unsuitable for mass production in war. *Wellington* is afloat on the Thames as a clubhouse but little of her original appearance or

equipment survives. At the time of writing (2007) there is a serious proposal to bring *Whimbrel* back from Egypt and make her a Battle of the Atlantic memorial at Liverpool. She has not changed much from wartime appearance.

Trawlers

Trawlers played only a very minor part in the Battle of the Atlantic but it is worth giving brief consideration to the reasons for this. During the 1932 review of ASW, a shortage of coastal escorts was identified. The Admiralty took two positive steps to remedy this situation with prototypes of a converted commercial trawler and a new design built in the style of a commercial trawler, but with changes to make her more suitable as a coastal A/S escort.

The *James Ludford* had been built for the Admiralty during World War I as one of sixty-nine *Mersey* class but was entirely typical of a commercial trawler of her generation. She was given a 4in gun, asdic type 123 and twenty-five depth charges with two rails and two throwers. Sadly, she was sunk by a mine in December 1939.

Basset was the prototype for 211 vessels of the Dance, Isles, Tree and Shakespeare classes built during the war, including sixteen in Canada and eighteen in India. The structure

Unst was typical of a very numerous group of Admiralty designs based on trawler practice.

was based on commercial trawler practice but the hull form was 'warship' style, based on model tests. Subdivision was much improved over commercial ships and accommodation somewhat better.

Table 1.6: Trawler *James Ludford*
Displacement (tons): 438, 665 deep
Dimensions (feet): 138½ pp x 23¾ x 13½ mld
Speed (kts): 11
Fuel (tons), endurance (miles) @ (kts):
Complement: 20

Table 1.7: Trawler *Basset*
Displacement (tons): 551, 775 deep
Dimensions (feet): 150 pp x 27½ x 13½ aft
Speed (kts): 13
Endurance (miles) @ (kts): 3,000 @ 9
Complement: 33

A Type VIIC U-boat at the war's end. Deep diving and reliable, they were the backbone of Dönitz's fleet.

During the war some 100 trawlers were converted into ocean escorts. Such ships were at least 160 feet long with a speed of eleven to twelve knots. Typically they would carry 200 tons of coal, enough for fourteen days' steaming at economical speed, with three days' reserve. They would have a 4in gun and one to three Oerlikons, with asdic in the 123 series, Type 268 PQ radar, four depth charge throwers, two rails and fifty-five charges. The armament fit was little inferior to a Flower and many escorts failed to match their endurance. They were seaworthy enough for fishing off Iceland. Why then did they feature so little in the Atlantic?

It was probably a combination of things. For example, in many requisitioned ships the deck over the hold was in bad condition and, where possible, it was replaced with a steel deck. However, in many ships stability was insufficient to permit this. No stability data were available for most ships and many were inclined. A minimum value of GM was set at twelve inches, with a freeboard of thirty inches in the larger vessels. Stability demanded ballast, whilst freeboard made this difficult. Extra equipment was mainly topweight and made stability worse. Lack of space for new, improved asdics and for radar, together with their crews, was probably the biggest factor. The crew of requisitioned trawlers was about half that of a Flower, which led to rapid exhaustion, particularly with the severe motions of a smaller ship. A few were used as rescue ships.

U-boats
A study of any of the standard reference books[29] will suggest that there were few technical developments in U-boat design between the wars. A typical comparison is shown in table 1.8. There are, however, two important omissions from this table: diving depth and sensor fit. In both cases they were seen as very important and hence were kept secret

Table 1.8: Comparison of U-boat specifications from the two world wars

Boat	Date	Displacement (tons)	Length (m)	Speed (kts) surface	submerged*	Gun (mm)	Torpedo tubes no.	dia.(mm)	Crew	Range (nm)/speed (kts)
U-161	1918	820	71.6	16.8	8.6	105	6	500	39	8,500/10
U-69	1939	749	67.1	17	7.6	88	5	533	44	8,500/8

* For one hour

but, to some extent, their significance has not always been appreciated by modern writers.

In shallow waters, such as those round the British Isles, it is necessary only to know the position of a target submarine in plan – two dimensions. In deeper waters the problem becomes a much more complicated, three-dimensional one. A related problem is that it takes a long while for a depth charge to sink to the level of the submarine, making the fire control problem more difficult and increasing the opportunity for the boat to move out of lethal distance from the charge.

A different problem is the meaning of 'diving depth'. One meaning is the depth at which the hull will collapse (see appendix I). This was calculated by an inexact formula and was subject to errors in building, while control errors mean that a submarine may not hold the intended depth.

For all these reasons a large factor of safety was applied in setting an operational maximum depth. Some idea of the depths involved may be seen in comparing figures for the Royal Navy's S class. British practice of the day was to apply a factor of safety of about 2. Initially the Germans used a similar factor. Submarine COs were aware of this and would usually test dive to 10 per cent below the 'safe' depth. Designers were aware of

A Type XI U-boat, bigger and longer-ranged than the Type VII.

this and even encouraged it on trials, having added 10 per cent to the safety margin. I have even noted reputable writers compare British safe depth with German collapse depth. In table 1.9, depths listed as 'trial' are those achieved in post-war trials when submarines were lowered until they collapsed.

Table 1.9: Collapse depth, S class			
	Safe (feet)	Calculated (feet)	Trial (feet)
Early, riveted boats	300	534	530
Welded boats	350	700	650

German designers of the mid-1930s had the advantage of a more accurate method of calculating the strength of pressure hulls and framing. This enabled them to use lighter framing than British boats, putting the weight saved into thicker plating. They also had the benefit of weldable steel, thus saving more weight. The early Type VII U-boats were quoted as having a 100-metre safe depth and 200-metre collapse. It is likely that neither COs nor even designers were aware of the ultimate strength of these boats (see appendix I). COs soon found that the risk of exceeding 100 metres was much less than that of being within lethal range of a depth charge.

Post-war analysis suggests that the collapse depth of a Type VIIC was about 800 feet, though U-331 is said to have survived a dive to 876 feet. In the latter years of the war, 500 feet was used fairly frequently. The Type VIIC-41 had a thicker pressure hull, giving nominal diving depths of 120 metres and collapse at 250 metres, while the Type VIIC-42 was even thicker with depths of 200 metres and 400 metres. In both these latter classes the weight for the thicker pressure hull came mostly from lighter machinery. The Type IX and IXD had a diving depth of 100 metres and collapse at 200 metres, both often exceeded.

Particulars of the Type VIIC are given in table 1.8 (U-69). The bigger Type IX had a displacement (surface) of 1,144 tons and a length of 76.5 metres. They had four bow tubes and two stern. Surface speed was about eighteen knots. They were a development of the unsuccessful Type IA and very similar to the U-81 of 1915. It is said that Raeder was very enthusiastic for the bigger IXs, while Dönitz preferred the more manoeuvrable VIIs.

Nominal endurance is defined by fuel stowage: about 8,500 miles at ten knots for the VIIC from about 100 tons oil, 12,000 for the VIID from 160 tons of oil, and 13,850 at ten knots for Type IXC with 200 tons oil. This is an arbitrary figure and probably greater than would be achieved in war (see Type XIV U-boat, chapter 5). Effective endurance also depends on the number of torpedoes – eleven to twelve for VIIs, twenty-two for the IXs – and on supplies of food. U-boats would leave harbour with half their toilet cubicles full of tinned food and layers of tins on the floor of the passageway. Above all, endurance depended on that of the crew and there is no doubt of the dedication of U-boat men.

From about the date of the Anglo-German treaty the Germans decided to concentrate their acoustic work on passive (listening) sets. As a result, when war broke out, they had a mediocre active asdic set and a superb listening hydrophone. This was the Atlas-Werke GHG set used in wartime boats such as the Types VII and IX. Fittings varied slightly but in usual form there were forty-eight Rochelle salt hydrophones in two rows of horseshoe shape below the torpedo tubes. Typically, it could pick up a surface ship at ten miles, though a convoy could be heard at a greater distance. An escort coming in for a quiet attack at slow speed could usually be detected by the noise from her auxiliary machinery. The potential of this set was only recognised in August 1941 with the capture of U-570 (HMS *Graph*). In listening capability it was far superior to RN asdic in passive mode.

A Type VIIC, U-995, forms part of the U-boat war memorial near Kiel, while a Type IX, U-505, is shown at the Chicago Museum of Science. Type XIV (milch cows) and Type XXI are dealt with later. Both the Types IX and VII were excellent conventional submarines with pressure hulls stronger than those of other navies.

2 War, the First Phase:
September 1939–April 1940

Both Britain and Germany made important preliminary moves before fighting broke out on 1 September with the invasion of Poland. The RN's Home Fleet, which had been exercising from Invergordon, now moved to its old-time base at Scapa Flow, still largely unprotected from attack. A well-timed review of the Reserve Fleet had been held in Weymouth Bay during August, ensuring that the old destroyers of the V&W classes would have crews and that their machinery was tested and ready.

British operations were directed by the C-in-C Plymouth, Adm Sir M Dunbar-Nasmith, VC, an outstanding submarine commander of World War I. Like so many senior service officers of democracies at the opening of a war, he had to tackle a difficult task with totally inadequate resources. However, he founded the training organisations at Liverpool and Tobermory (see chapter 3) and planned the move of Western Approaches Command to Derby House, Liverpool. His successors owed much to his

PC74 was built in World War I as a P boat with merchant-ship appearance. She was used as the decoy ship *Chatsgrove* in early World War II, with no success, before reverting to auxiliary duties. (IWM A 25975)

preparatory work.

Germany had fifty-seven U-boats – almost exactly the intelligence estimate – on the outbreak of war, a very small proportion of the 300 Atlantic boats that Dönitz saw as needed to win a war on merchant shipping. Of these boats, thirty-nine were operational, the remainder being used for training or working up after completion. Another six were due to complete by the end of 1939. Between 15 and 19 August eighteen U-boats sailed for their war stations – five small Type IIC and thirteen Type VIIA or B. This was a maximum-effort deployment before the British were able to introduce counter-measures such as convoy. The 'pocket battleship' *Graf Spee* sailed from Wilhelmshaven on 21 August, followed by the *Deutschland* three days later, accompanied by their supply ships *Altmark* and *Westerwald*. The Admiralty saw these surface raiders as a greater threat than the submarine.

In these early days Hitler still hoped for a short war against Poland, followed by a negotiated peace with Britain and France. In consequence, Dönitz was ordered to operate strictly within the Prize Rules, forbidding attacks on merchant ships without warning. Unfortunately for any such hopes, Lemp in U-30 sighted a liner in poor visibility that, from its position and movements, he thought wrongly to be an armed merchant cruiser. He fired two torpedoes, both of which hit and exploded, an unusual success rate. He had sunk the Donaldson liner *Athenia* of 13,851grt, carrying some 1,100 passengers, of which over 300 were Americans. Despite prompt rescue attempts 112 were drowned, including 28 Americans. The Nazi command made frantic efforts to conceal the involvement of a German submarine, while the British drew the parallel with *Lusitania*. Propaganda apart, the government and the RN saw this as a clear indication that Germany intended to wage unrestricted submarine war from the start. It is probable that this misinterpretation made little difference, as submarine warfare 'to the rules' is so difficult that an accident was almost bound to happen. Initially, the German command re-emphasised the need to observe the Prize Rules, but on 24 September Dönitz ordered that ships using their radio should be sunk without further warning.

As discussed in the previous chapter, the Admiralty had well worked-out plans for convoys, though it was not intended to implement them until it was clear that Germany had adopted unrestricted warfare. The sinking of *Athenia* was taken as such confirmation and convoys began to operate. One convoy had jumped the gun: eight tankers, bound for the Gulf, had been held at Gibraltar until Italy's intentions became clear. They left on the long trip round Africa on 2 September under cruiser escort as far as Freetown.

Convoy OA1 of seventeen ships bound for North America left the Downs on 7 September, while OB1 of ten ships left Liverpool the same day. Coming the other way, HX1 of fifteen ships left Halifax, Nova Scotia[1] on 16 September, followed by a fast convoy, HXF1, on the 29th. The speed of HX convoys was set at nine knots, though eight knots was more typical of that achieved. HXF convoys were for ships that were faster but could not achieve the fifteen knots set for independents. The speed for SC convoys, slow passages from Cape Breton, was set at seven and a half to eight knots. These early convoys were small in numbers of merchant ships but within a month or so built up to the thirty to forty ships then thought optimum. The times of passage for the main routes were:

HX	15.2 days from New York
SC	15.4 days from Sydney, Cape Breton
SL	19 days from Freetown

Under Dunbar-Nasmith, many of the measures that would lead to victory were initiated. The escort force for these convoys was often only a single destroyer and a sloop, with little training or experience in ASW, which remained with the convoy only as far as 15°W. Fast ships sailed independently, as it was thought that a submarine with a maximum surface speed of about seventeen knots, reduced in bad weather, would not be able to attack. The lower limit of speed to sail independently was set at fifteen knots, reduced to thirteen in November 1940. During September, forty-eight merchant ships were sunk by U-boats, of which forty-three were sailing independently, and only one from convoy (the others were mined). Lowering the qualifying speed made matters dramatically worse. On the Halifax route, the chance of an escorted ship's being sunk on a round voyage was 5.8 per cent, whilst that for an independent (thirteen to fifteen knots) was 13.8 per cent.

Various attempts were made to remedy the shortage of escort vessels. The idea of 'Q' ships, which had some success in World War I, was resurrected. By March 1940, eight decoy ships were fitted out with up to nine 4in guns, torpedo tubes and depth charges.[2] They were to simulate a straggler and catch a U-boat unawares, and

even to take on a surface raider with some prospect of causing damage. None of them had any success and two were lost. An enquiry was held in December 1940, as a result of which the scheme was abandoned.

The Admiralty was still worried by the potential threat from surface raiders and by February 1940 forty-six armed merchant cruisers had been commissioned. Most convoys in more distant waters had an escort of a single such ship, though since most had obsolete guns, little or no fire control and crews made up of reservists and National Service youths, their prospects in a duel with a raider were not good.

The Admiralty, egged on by the First Lord,

Gardenia was a very early Flower and unusual in completing with two masts.

Churchill, had fallen for the old fallacy that escorting convoys was 'defensive' and that we should go on the 'offensive' with hunting groups, 'like cavalry'. A pre-war study by the Tactical Division of the Staff had proposed nineteen groups, each of five ships with air support (some from fleet carriers). With only about 100 escort vessels available, this would have left few for convoy work. Some hunting groups were formed, a very few including a fleet carrier. A comparison of the one-mile effective range of asdic with the 3,000-mile expanse of the Atlantic Ocean should have shown the folly of this approach. Later, with submarine concentrations localised by Enigma and plenty of escorts, hunting made sense.

On 14 September U-39 sighted *Ark Royal* off Orkney and fired two torpedoes from an ideal position at a range of 800 yards. Both exploded prematurely some eighty yards short. This revealed the position of U-39, and the destroyer *Foxhound* leapt to the attack, blowing the submarine to the surface and capturing her crew in the first U-boat sinking of the war. The next day, two Skuas from *Ark Royal* attacked U-30, causing superficial damage, but the explosion of the bombs before reaching the sea caused both aircraft to crash. Two of the aircrew were rescued by the submarine.

On 17 September U-31 sighted the carrier *Courageous*, which was hunting submarines with four destroyers. Two of these were detached to investigate a visual sighting by one of her aircraft some seventy miles from the carrier leaving only two destroyers as escort and planeguard. A change of course put U-31 in an ideal attacking position at a range of about 3,000 yards. She fired three torpedoes, of which two hit, sinking the carrier with the loss of 518 men – and one of the RN's five carriers.[3] This put an end to the practice of using fleet carriers to hunt submarines but it was another year or two before the Admiralty stopped taking escorts from the screen to prosecute a contact some hours' steaming away.

A month later, on 14 October, Prien took his U-47 through an unblocked channel into Scapa Flow and sank the battleship *Royal Oak*. Prien was a brilliant and dedicated U-boat officer and a fanatical Nazi, who would become one of the most successful U-boat commanders of the war. He had visited Orkney as a 'tourist' before the war and studied the entrances to Scapa Flow.

Coastal Command of the RAF was unable to offer much in the way of air support. Of a force of seventeen squadrons, only one squadron of Hudsons and two of Sunderland flying boats had sufficient endurance to operate over the Atlantic convoy routes. The majority of the Command's aircraft were Ansons, with insufficient endurance even to reach the coast of Norway, and a load of four ineffective 100lb bombs. To be fair to the Air Ministry, they had been told by the Admiralty before the war that the submarine threat had been neutralised and that the main threat to shipping came from surface raiders. An anti-submarine bomb had been developed, starting in 1925, which entered service in 1931. An 'improved' Mk III was adopted, without trials, in 1934. There were three sizes – 100lb, 250lb and 500lb – all suffering from a fuse which was virtually useless and an unpredictable underwater trajectory. In September the British submarine *Snapper* was hit by a 100lb bomb dropped by an Anson. The bomb hit at the base of the conning tower, causing no structural damage but breaking four light bulbs. The 250lb bomb was claimed to be lethal at six feet from the target, and the 500lb at eight feet.

Coastal Command's greatest asset in the early days was its commander-in-chief, Sir Frederick Bowhill. He had entered the Navy in 1904, transferring to the RNAS and following it into the RAF in 1918. He understood the ways of ships and the sea but with an airman's eye.[4]

Problems

During a war, staffs tend to underestimate the problems of their enemy and this fault is even more common amongst the works of later analysts, despite the benefit of hindsight. During the opening phase of this war, both sides had plenty of problems. Common to both was a shortage of vessels with which to implement their plans. Dönitz had more direct problems. The engines of the Type VII seem to have given trouble and their engine mounts needed stiffening urgently. These problems were not serious but exposed weakness in the refit organisation.

The torpedoes fired by the U-boats had much more serious problems.[5] In the 1930s Germany had developed two types of torpedo: the G7a and the G7e. The former was a good, conventional torpedo running on compressed air and Decalin (decahydronapthalene). It had a 300kg warhead and three speed settings up to forty-four knots, at which it had a range of 6,000 metres. The forty-four-knot setting was temporarily deleted early in the war but reinstated after the engine was modified.

The G7e had an electric drive with a battery weighing 665kg, which gave a speed of thirty knots for a range of 5,000 metres; but there was no bubble track. It was developed in great secrecy at Karlskrona (Sweden) from 1929 and its existence was unknown to the RN until remains were found close to the wreck of the *Royal Oak* in Scapa Flow. Full details came with the capture of U-570 in August 1941. Other than the lack of a bubble track, the great advantage of the electric torpedo was that it was easier and cheaper to manufacture. In 1939 a G7a required 3,730 man-hours, reduced to 1,707 by 1943, whereas the G7e needed only 1,255 man-hours. Production of all types of submarine-launched torpedoes (mainly G7e) was at the rate of seventy per month in 1939, rising to 1,000 a month by early 1941, peaking at 1,700 by 1943 and falling back to 1,400 in 1944.

The first problem to become apparent was in depth-keeping, with frequent examples of torpedoes running up to 3.7 metres too deep. This problem had been recognised before the war but was not taken too seriously, as it was expected that the magnetic firing pistol would normally be used, and thus a small depth error would not matter. The problem was found to be a build-up of pressure in the balance chamber controlling depth-keeping through the hydroplanes. This was due to leakage from the air inside the submarine, which inevitably increased in pressure during submergence due to high-pressure air leaks, inboard venting, etc. Once this was diagnosed, better seals were provided and the problem was solved.

The MZ magnetic pistol had its own problems. It was oversensitive to changes in the perceived magnetic field and could be triggered by rapid manoeuvres of the torpedo and by local magnetic anomalies, which were common off Norway. Degaussing, as used by the British as protection against magnetic mines, also much reduced the distance at which the pistol would function. There was no easy solution and the magnetic pistol was deactivated until the end of 1942. This, in turn, exposed the failings of the contact pistol, which did not function when hitting at an oblique angle. RN magnetic pistols had similar problems but the fallback contact pistol was very reliable – so much so that the Germans considered copying the one they captured in *Seal*.

Mine Warfare

The RN soon closed the English Channel by laying 10,000 mines in both shallow and deep fields supported by patrols. The mines were of the World War I 'H II' type, but still effective.[6] After losing three Type II boats to these mines, Dönitz forbade the use of this route, so that all U-boats had to go round the north of Scotland. The Type IIs had insufficient endurance and operated in the North Sea, where they were exposed to the East Coast Barrage. An attempt to lay a new Northern Barrage was unsuccessful and uncompleted when the Germans invaded Norway. There was an attempt to mine the route to Greenland and Iceland, which was also unsuccessful, as was a field in St George's Channel.

On the other hand, mines laid by U-boats had some notable successes. The cruiser *Belfast* broke her back and suffered severe shock damage on a mine laid by U-21 on 21 November,[7] while *Nelson* was badly damaged, with many casualties, by a mine from U-31 on 4 December 1939. (*Nelson* suffered a large number of casualties from broken porcelain toilet pans.) Pre-war trials had shown the problems of shock damage but there was no time for remedial action before war broke out. These trials were conducted on a short pontoon and failed to show the effects of whipping. Up to the end of February, thirty-seven merchant ships totalling 129,000 tons had been sunk by submarine-laid mines.

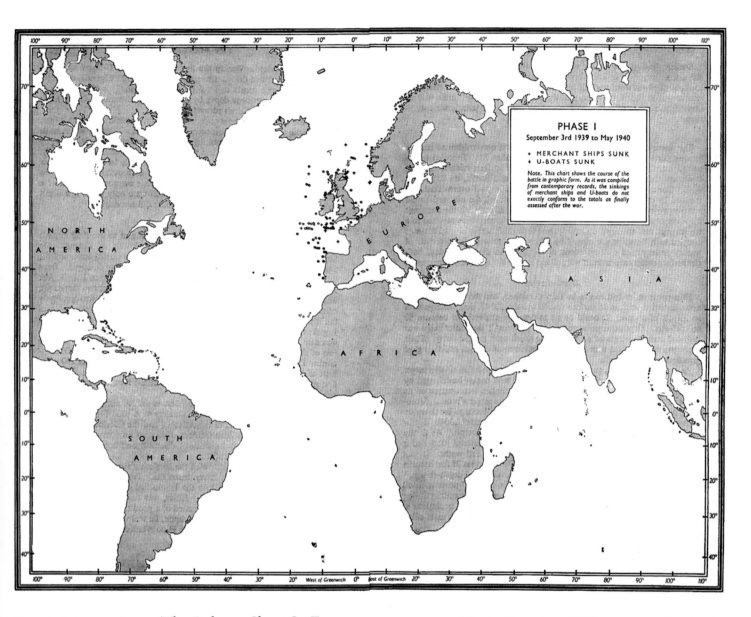

PHASE I
September 3rd 1939 to May 1940

• MERCHANT SHIPS SUNK
+ U-BOATS SUNK

Note. This chart shows the course of the battle in graphic form. As it was compiled from contemporary records, the sinkings of merchant ships and U-boats do not exactly conform to the totals as finally assessed after the war.

Phase 1 of the Atlantic battle. The pre-war view that attacks would take place mainly in or close to home waters was justified, the south-western approaches being the main danger zone.

The Balance Sheet So Far

Both sides had grounds for reasonable satisfaction on the way things had gone, but both had continuing problems and entertained hopes for better things to come. For both Britain and Germany the outstanding problem lay in shortage of numbers. Dönitz had asked for twenty-nine new boats per month but was forced to accept a target of twenty-five. It made little difference, as during the first half of 1940 only two boats were delivered each month, rising to six in the second half of the year. U-boat building was given priority from mid-1940. This was not enough to make up for losses, and the number of boats available for operations fell from thirty-

eight in December 1939 to twenty-five in the following November. The number on station was remarkably constant at one-third of the total, say six to eight.

On the British side, matters improved slightly as hunting groups were abandoned, making more vessels available for convoy escort. The only new escorts coming forward in numbers were the Hunt class destroyers, whose endurance was inadequate for Atlantic duties, and the Flower class corvettes, considered in the next section.

Up to May 1940, twenty-four U-boats had been sunk (see table 2.1). All the sinkings by surface ships resulted from depth charge attack.

One was by an old sloop, one by a minesweeper and the rest by destroyers.

Table 2.1: Causes of U-boat sinkings to May 1940	
Surface vessels	13½*
Aircraft	2½
Submarine	3
Mines	4
Accident and unknown**	1
Total	24
* ½ indicates shared	
** In this and later tables it is reasonable to assume that some losses with unknown cause were due to mines	

Sinkings of merchant ships by U-boats fluctuated considerably, mainly because of the small numbers involved. In the months up to March 1940, when the U-boats redeployed for the Norwegian campaign, the average tonnage sunk per month was some 160,000–180,000grt, of which 60 per cent were ships sailing independently. This represented 57,000 tons per U-boat sunk, nearly as low as in 1918 when the first U-boat war was lost. In the first few months of the war, losses of merchant ships had been made good by some new building and a 'one off' bonus of captured German shipping. Dönitz was not unduly worried, as things could only improve as more U-boats entered service. This was the war the Admiralty had planned for and, by and large, they got it right.

Asdic in Use

The introduction of asdic[8] led to a major change in anti-submarine warfare (ASW): for the first time a fully submerged submarine could be detected and located with sufficient accuracy for weapons to be launched with a reasonable promise of success. It is no reflection on the pioneers of asdic to point out that sets in use in 1939 had a number of limitations, some serious. Some of these problems were eliminated during the war by improved hardware, while the effect of others was reduced by improved operational methods. Most of the problems were known to specialists before the war and action was in hand. However, to many officers, asdic was a wonder weapon and knowledge of its limitations came as a great shock.

The transducer generated a short and narrow pulse of very high frequency sound, which would be reflected back if it hit a solid object. To aid interpretation, the pulse was represented by audible-frequency sound, the outgoing pulse emanating from the loudspeaker as a 'ping'. The beam was quite narrow – 5° – and the operator had to wait for the reflection before moving to the next 5° sector. It could take a long while to search a wide arc and the submarine could move a considerable way between pulses. More numerous escorts reduced the arc that each had to search, while

This composite drawing by John Roberts shows (a) The conical beam of the main set (120 series), effective out to 2,500 yards in good conditions but with no ability to measure depth. It was not able to detect submarines at great depth.
(b) The Q attachment, introduced to overcome these problems. It had a very narrow (3-degree) beam in the horizontal plane and only needed a very small strip below the main transducer.
(c) The 147 was a more advanced depth measuring set and was used to set the required depth on Squid projectiles immediately before firing.
See also Chapter 7 Page 114.

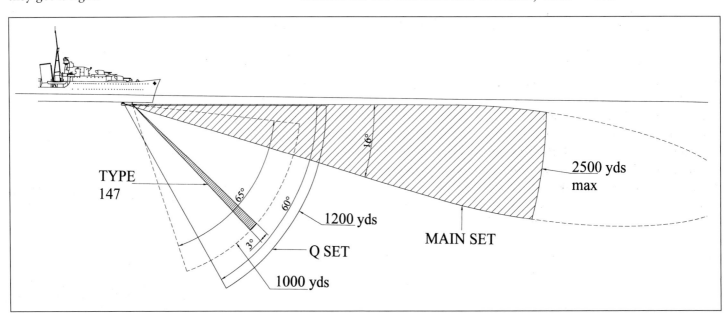

TYPE 147
65°
60°
3°
16°
1200 yds
1000 yds
Q SET
MAIN SET
2500 yds max

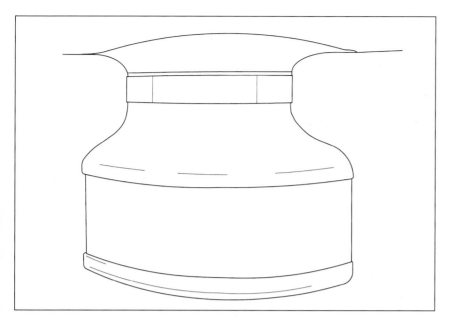

Asdic dome for Type 121 and typical of all early retractable domes. (John Roberts)

Right and over page top: The Mk VII depth charge was little changed from the Type D of World War I. Initially its charge was 290lb of amatol, but this was later changed to minol. Complete, it weighed 429lb. A faster-sinking version, Mk VII Heavy with an additional 150lb weight, was later introduced – as shown as an insert in the diagram. (John Lambert)

later sets could search more quickly.

If an echo was received, the range and bearing could be read off, the bearing recorder giving something of a moving image. These would be transferred to the plot, together with any data from other escorts, and the course and speed of the target determined. With early wartime asdics, the average detection range was about 1,300 yards, with 2,500 yards on occasional, good days. If the contact was stationary, it was probably not a submarine unless bottomed in shallow water. A moving echo could be received from a whale or a shoal of fish or even tide rips, though skilled operators could usually tell the character of the echo. The plot would distinguish between the erratic movement of fish and the purposeful movements of a submarine.

Water moving over the face of the transducer could generate noise, so from early days the transducer was carried within a water-filled, streamlined dome so that the water in contact was not moving. The dome was of light construction so that it did not obstruct or distort the sound beam, but this meant that it could not be exposed to the water pressure at high speeds. In consequence, the dome was made retractable, which gave serious problems. Ideally, it should be on the centre line, which meant cutting away the keel over a considerable length, but available structural design methods were unable to cope

with such a discontinuity in the area of peak slamming pressures. In slow-speed ships, retractable domes were not needed and the dome could be removed in dock. Such domes were often referred to as 'trawler sets'. Asdic was so secret that its importance was not explained to the ship designers, a common problem even today.

The sound beam spread in a cone shape from the transducer with the axis of the cone at an angle below the horizontal. This gave the only indication of target depth. The deeper the submarine, the greater the range at which it would enter the leading edge of the beam. As the escort got close to the submarine, the target would come out from the rear of the beam giving a further indication of depth but adding to the dead time before weapons – depth charges – could reach the target. The dead time would be from the time contact was lost till the stern depth charge rails were over the submarine, together with the time for the depth charges to sink to the estimated depth.

The Mk VII depth charge, basically the Type D of World War I, sank at an initial rate of 7ft/sec, accelerating to 9.9ft/sec at 250 feet. It weighed 429lb and carried a charge of 290lb of amatol (later minol; TNT filling was used in hot climates), which it was thought would be lethal if exploding within thirty feet of the submarine. In fact the lethal distance was more like twenty feet, though an explosion forty feet away might force the U-boat to surface. Since depth estimation was

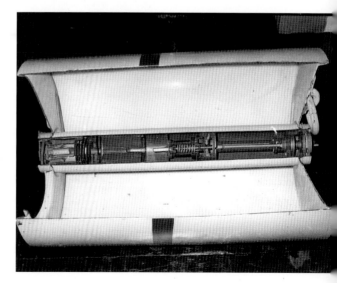

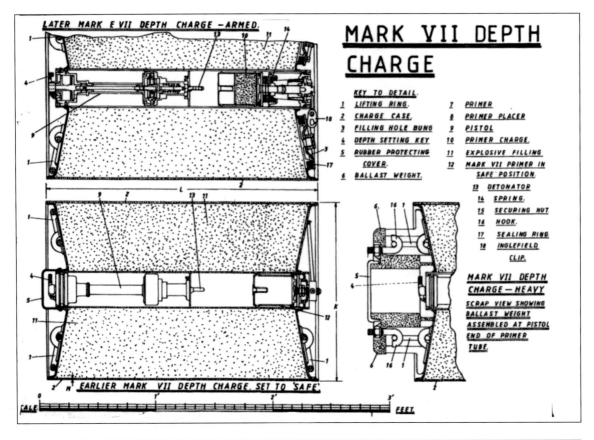

MARK VII DEPTH CHARGE

KEY TO DETAIL.

1	LIFTING RING.	7	PRIMER
2	CHARGE CASE.	8	PRIMER PLACER
3	FILLING HOLE BUNG	9	PISTOL
4	DEPTH SETTING KEY	10	PRIMER CHARGE.
5	RUBBER PROTECTING	11	EXPLOSIVE FILLING
	COVER.	12	MARK VII PRIMER IN
6	BALLAST WEIGHT.		SAFE POSITION.
		13	DETONATOR
		14	SPRING.
		15	SECURING NUT
		16	HOOK.
		17	SEALING RING.
		18	INGLEFIELD
			CLIP.

MARK VII DEPTH CHARGE – HEAVY
SCRAP VIEW SHOWING BALLAST WEIGHT ASSEMBLED AT PISTOL END OF PRIMER TUBE.

The original depth charge thrower, the Mk II (*top right and far right*). The carrier and stalk were thrown with the charge, which was wasteful in weight and storage space. It was later replaced by the Mk IV (*centre right and far right*) in which the carrier and stalk were retained. (John Lambert)

Depth charge stowage rack. (John Lambert)

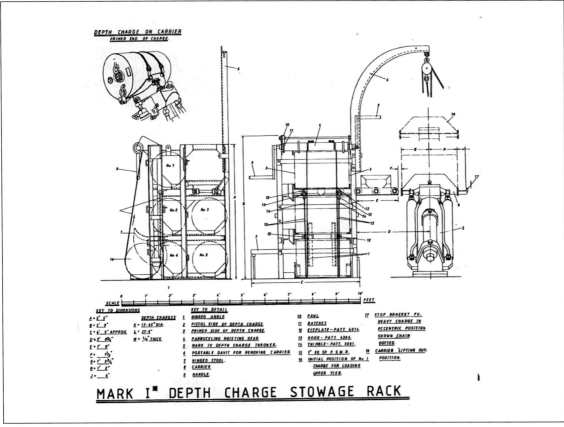

MARK I* DEPTH CHARGE STOWAGE RACK

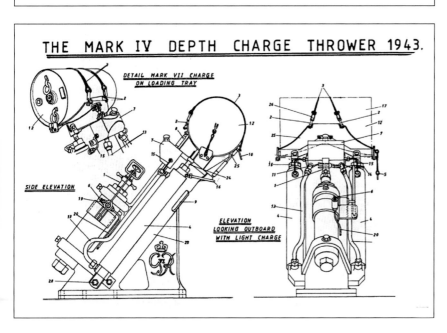

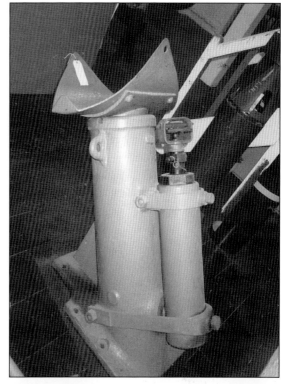

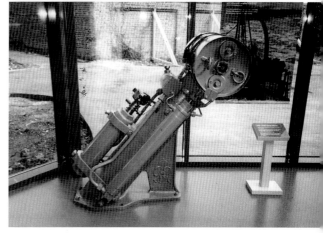

only slightly better than guesswork, the chance of a successful attack was remote; in the first six months of the war 4,000 attacks were made, sinking thirty-three U-boats – less than 1 per cent. By 1943–4, better training and improved equipment brought the chance of a successful depth charge attack to about 5 per cent.

The dead time is a key aspect of anti-submarine warfare in World War II. The sinking time to 250 feet was about thirty-five seconds, to which must be added some twenty to twenty-five seconds for loss of contact (typically 200 yards),

a total of nearly a minute. At four knots (5ft/sec) a submarine could move 300 feet in any direction, far in excess of the lethal distance of some thirty feet. The deeper the U-boat, the longer the time required for the depth charge to sink and the less likely a kill. The seriousness of this problem had been partly concealed in pre-war exercises in the Portland area, where the sea is fairly shallow.

The sea is not uniform in density. Differences in salinity and temperature cause differences in density, which lead to changes in sound transmis-

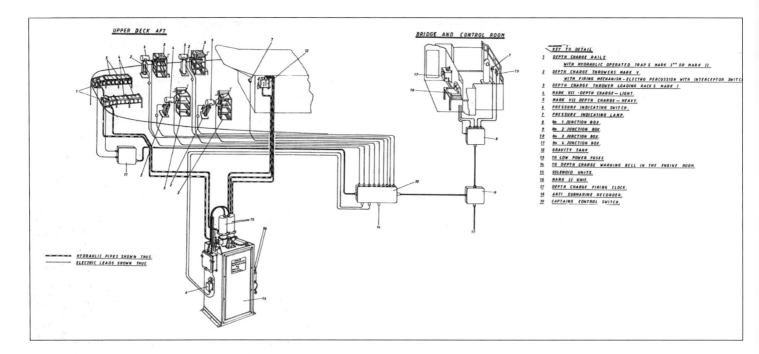

UPPER DECK AFT

BRIDGE AND CONTROL ROOM

KEY TO DETAIL
1 DEPTH CHARGE RAILS
   WITH HYDRAULIC OPERATED TRAPS MARK I** OR MARK II.
2 DEPTH CHARGE THROWERS MARK V.
   WITH FIRING MECHANISM - ELECTRO PERCUSSION WITH INTERCEPTOR SWITCH
3 DEPTH CHARGE THROWER LOADING RACKS MARK I
4 MARK VII DEPTH CHARGE - LIGHT.
5 MARK VII DEPTH CHARGE - HEAVY.
6 PRESSURE INDICATING SWITCH.
7 PRESSURE INDICATING LAMP.
8 No 1 JUNCTION BOX
9 No 2 JUNCTION BOX
10 No 3 JUNCTION BOX
11 No 4 JUNCTION BOX
12 GRAVITY TANK
13 TO LOW POWER FUSES
14 TO DEPTH CHARGE WARNING BELL IN THE ENGINE ROOM.
15 SOLENOID UNITS.
16 MARK II UNIT.
17 DEPTH CHARGE FIRING CLOCK.
18 ANTI SUBMARINE RECORDER.
19 CAPTAINS CONTROL SWITCH.

HYDRAULIC PIPES SHOWN THUS.
ELECTRIC LEADS SHOWN THUS

sion that can bend a sound beam as a lens or prism bends a light beam.

The basic depth charge pattern was the diamond, with a charge at each corner and one in the middle, all set to the same depth. Initially the charges were forty yards apart, but after studies at Fairlie this was increased to sixty yards in 1943 when amatol was replaced by minol. In late 1940 the Mk VII Heavy was introduced, with a 150lb weight attached, which sank at 16ft/sec and had a minol charge, lethal at twenty-six feet and disabling at twice that distance. Using two rails and four throwers it was possible to drop a total of ten charges, mixed heavy and light, which would explode as two diamond patterns, fifty feet apart in depth – the 'ten pattern'. The full pattern for a mean depth of seventy-five feet began with a heavy charge from the rail followed three seconds later by two heavies from the forward throwers and a light from the rails. After a further eight seconds, the after throwers discharged two lights with a heavy from the rails, and then the remaining charges from the rails. Later, a fourteen pattern was tried, but with only a total of 100 charges or less carried in most ships the ten pattern was seen as the best compromise. Initially the ex-Brazilian Hs had eight throwers and three rails, capable of launching seventeen charges.

The one-ton Mk 10 was introduced in December 1942. With a charge of 2,000lb, it was said to be as effective as a ten pattern of Mk VIIs and better at depth. It was fired from a torpedo tube in destroyers and a special launching rail in the Captains. Early versions sank at 6ft/sec to give time for the dropping ship to get clear, later increased to 21ft/sec with a depth setting of 640 feet. It was determined that the ship should be safe at eleven knots with a depth setting of 220 feet. The weapon seems to have been used only rarely. The original thrower Mk II was replaced by the Mk IV from September 1941, which retained the arbor on which the charge rested.

This diagram by John Lambert shows the complex electric and hydraulic systems needed to fire a ten-pattern charge under asdic control.

This is the meaning of 'lethal damage': the effect of an underwater explosion on the submarine *Stygian* in a post-war trial.

Flower Class Corvettes

By 1938 it was clear that there were too few escort vessels, both for ocean work and, more urgently, for the east coast. The points made in the review of 1932 remained valid but the threat was clear and growing, as were the problems. Rearmament had started but this made matters worse for the building of numerous escorts, as the traditional builders of ships and engines were all working to capacity and beyond.

Two memoranda, summarised here, by Sir Stanley Goodall in early 1939 shed light on options for cheap A/S vessels as war approached. Consideration had already been given to the use of commercial whale catchers. These needed much more alteration than trawlers because of their poor subdivision and there must be some doubt regarding the quoted cost of £50,000, which may have referred to 1936 when prices were much lower. Alterations to convert existing ships would be extensive and costly.

Experience in the First World War showed that the requirements for A/S vessels increased in both size and speed from 42-ton MLs to twenty-two-knot, 573-ton P boats. USN experience was similar in starting with 110-feet submarine chasers before the 590-ton Eagles with a speed of twenty-two knots. Speed is expensive but it is an unwise economy to build slower ships than the submarines capable of eighteen knots on the surface that are being built by hostile powers.

Two factors of importance to consider in connection with the type of A/S vessels contemplated for construction during wartime are the source of production and the time for building. These two factors are inter-connected. Ships such as the Admiralty design based on trawler practice could be built rapidly because the machinery is simple and the yards concerned are merchant ship builders specialising in this type of work; whereas ships like patrol vessels [*Kingfishers*] with more complex machinery should preferably be built in yards that would be busy with other warship work.[9]

MTBs fitted for A/S work [MASB] seem most suited for local work. Their first cost is low but life of light, fast craft is short and engines will be a problem.

Ancestor of the Flower class, the World War I escort *Kilbeggan*. Some of this class were built by Smith's Dock.

Consideration should be given to a heavy lift ship as base. The cost might be £350,000 which makes motor boat solution less cheap. Larger motor boats with more endurance and better living conditions might be better. If required could order a prototype for trials, particularly with asdic.[10]

It is possible that the genesis of the Fairmile A may be discerned in this memorandum.

Options for 'Cheap' A/S Vessels[11]

Conversion of commercial trawler. About 620 tons, 11–12 knots. Coal burning, cylindrical boiler and single reciprocating engine. Endurance about 3,500 at 9 knots. Complement 24. They were moderate asdic platforms but had inadequate subdivision. Conversion would take 4 weeks and cost £35,000.

Admiralty trawler. 510 tons. 11¾–12½ knots. Coal burning, cylindrical boiler and single reciprocating engine. Endurance 3,500 at 9 knots. Complement 24. Good asdic platform with adequate subdivision. They would take 4 months to build and cost £57,000.

Converted whale catcher (*Southern Pride*). 700 tons, 16 knots. Oil fuel, two boilers, one reciprocating engine. Endurance 4,000 at 12 knots. Complement 30. Moderate asdic platform, subdivision bad. Conversion would take 6 weeks and cost £75,000.

New whale catcher to Admiralty requirements. 900 tons, 16 knots. Oil fuel, two boilers, one reciprocating engine. Endurance 4,000 at 12 knots. Complement 30. Good asdic platform with adequate subdivision. They would take 7 months to build and cost £90,000.

A/S version of *Bangor*. 500 tons, 17 knots. Oil fuel, two boilers, turbines (alternative diesel). Endurance 4,000 at 10 knots. Complement 50. Good asdic platform and good subdivision. They would take 8 months to build and cost £135,000.

Simplified *Guillemot*. 580 tons, 20–1 knots. Oil fuel, two boilers, geared turbines. Endurance 3,000 at 11 knots. Complement 63. Good asdic platform and good subdivision. They would take 8 months to build and cost £160,000.

Hunt class. 890 tons, 29 knots. Endurance 3,500 at 20 knots. Oil fuel, two boilers, geared turbines. Complement 144. Good asdic platform and good subdivision. They would take 12 months to build and cost £400,000.

Southern Gem was typical of the big whale catchers built by Smith's Dock. She is shown in 1942 fitted for A/S duties.

It was noted that all would be 'seaworthy craft capable of hard work' but not equal. Similarly they were 'vessels in which men can live in reasonable conditions' but again not equal. Protection depended on transverse subdivision and the commercial trawler and whale catcher were 'very unsatisfactory' in that regard. Time and cost figures are relative. Note the cost of *Guillemot*, far larger than usually quoted. Faced with these figures, the Board chose option 4, which developed into the Flower class – and who can blame them?

The problem was still seen, particularly in respect of coastal work on the east coast. The little coastal sloops of the *Kingfisher* class were capable – and beautiful – but rather shallow for asdic work and far too expensive (*Kingfisher* cost £160,000) to build in numbers. They displaced 550 tons, coming under a clause of the London Treaty permitting unrestricted building of vessels under 600 tons. Trawlers, particularly those of Admiralty design developed from *Basset*, were cheap and useful but their speed of twelve and a half knots and short endurance limited their ASW capability, as did their size. Something bigger but still cheap was needed.

It seems that ideas were sought from several builders but details have only survived for the successful candidate from Smith's Dock. This was a well-known shipbuilder on the Tees specialising in fishing vessels and most notable for its whale catchers. Their managing director, Mr W Reed, pointed out that they had been building A/S vessels since the 'Zed' whalers of 1915, followed by the 'Kil' class boats, also of World War I. These 'Kils' were originally intended to have oil-fired, water-tube boilers for a speed of seventeen to eighteen knots, remarkably similar to the Flowers of World War II. However, oil was scarce, as were skilled personnel, and they completed with coal-fired Scotch-type boilers and a speed of fourteen knots.

Reed's first proposal in 1938 was based closely on the whale catcher *Southern Pride*, lengthened by thirty feet. There was a meeting in January 1939 at which Reed seems to have been given some degree of approval for a 700-ton ship costing £90,000. It then grew to 1,390 tons, mainly as a result of a change to coal burning. Fortunately, sanity returned and final approval was for an oil burner of 940 tons (standard). The DNC (Sir Stanley Goodall) was an enthusiastic supporter of the proposal, noting in his diary, 'I spoke against *Guillemot* and for whale catcher.'[12] Initially they were known as 'patrol vessels of whale catcher type'. The origin of the term 'corvette' is unclear; it is often said that Churchill chose it and this may well be true, though no evidence has been found to support this. Canadian sources attribute it to Adm Nelles, RCN. Both could be right. Historically it was a very unsuitable name, as a

The pretty *Mallard* was a possible alternative to the Flowers but was too expensive and used scarce turbine machinery.

corvette was much bigger than a sloop, but it had a fine ring to it.

At a meeting on 8 February 1939 Messrs Edwards and Reed of Smith's Dock drew attention to the performance of the steam trawler *Imperialist*, which they would guarantee for thirteen knots loaded with 1,050ihp (indicated horsepower) on wet steam.[13] DNC was not interested, as the extra speed was little more than the Admiralty design for which Smith's Dock were doing the drawings and the Admiralty design was easier to build. DNC was more interested in the whale catchers *Southern Pride* and *Sondra*. The drawbacks to these were poor subdivision and the bar keel. Reed thought he could produce an intermediate design with speed of fifteen to sixteen knots. It was agreed that he should look into the possibility and send an outline drawing and particulars of dimensions, speed and draught, and state time to build, cost and breakdown of equipment between ASI/commercial.

Dr Harland has pointed out[14] that the Flowers were far from a copy of the *Southern Pride*. They had a flat plate keel instead of the whale catchers' bar keel. Corvettes had bilge keels, inadequate in size at first. They were given a pair of stockless anchors and a windlass. A forecastle was added, forming a seamen's washplace, heads and stores. The mess deck was below and traditionalists were horrified that seamen and stokers messed together.

The bridge block was sited above the wardroom and two officers' cabins. On the lower level there was the CO's cabin and the officers' bathroom, with a wheelhouse above. On top there was an open bridge with an enclosed compass shelter. In early years there were many individual variations in bridge details but later most were altered to a standard design. The POs' mess was aft with the galley above, ensuring that food was cold before it reached the forward mess deck.

It was originally thought (1939) that these ships could be used to enforce the blockade on the Northern Patrol. To this end they were given a long-range radio that required two masts some distance apart. Six RN corvettes completed with the two-masted rig but many more retained the foremast ahead of the bridge, where it interfered with the view ahead. All early RCN ships had two masts.

The machinery was little changed from *Southern Pride*, a four-cylinder, triple-expansion engine driving a single shaft. Such engines were simple to build and within the capability of the

Spirea was an early British Flower. Note the open well deck abaft the forecastle ensuring that the crew got wet on the way to the bridge – and the galley was right aft.

Genista. This picture shows some of the aspects in which the Flowers departed from whaler practice. There was no bar keel, bilge keels were added – and later enlarged – and the bow shape differed. (Goss)

Cowslip. The censor has removed the pendant number but it may be read in the flag hoist (I learnt that trick at school during the war).

engineering departments of most shipyards. Smith's Dock supplied patterns to other builders and a total of 1,150 units were built for corvettes, frigates and transport ferries (LST 3). Shaft rpm was increased to 185, about the limit for a reciprocating engine lacking forced lubrication. At this speed the engine developed 2,750ihp giving a ship speed of sixteen knots, much faster than any trawler but less than a surfaced U-boat. The machinery was generally reliable, though the maintenance task was heavy. There were early problems with crankshaft

alignment, which led to some bearing failures. The majority had two Scotch-type boilers but those from Harland and Wolff had Howden Johnson units, and about twenty later ships (mostly Canadian) had water-tube boilers in closed stokeholds. The particulars of these war-winning engines were: stroke 30in; high-pressure diameter 18½in; medium-pressure 31in; both low-pressure 38½in.

Vibration can be a problem on fast-running reciprocating engines and they were balanced using the Yarrow Tweedy Slick method (based on

nineteenth-century torpedo boat work by Schlick). Later, one engine was used for a special vibration trial assisted by Lloyd's Register. The engine was decoupled from the drive shaft and run up to full speed to identify any critical rpm but no problems were found.

On trials, the first ship, *Gladiolus*, made 16.6 knots with 2,813ihp at 187 rpm on a displacement of 1,118 tons.[15] This equated to 16.5 knots at 2,750ihp and 185 rpm. Fuel consumption was 11.8 tons per 24 hours at 12 knots. Whale catchers need to be able to turn quickly, as do A/S ships using depth charges. The Flowers had the deadwood well cut away and a balanced rudder of 86 square feet. On trials at full speed they had an advance of 2.4 times the ship length and a tactical diameter of 2.1 lengths. Time to turn through 16 and 32 points was 51 and 109½ seconds respectively.

The large number involved, combined with cancellations and transfers, makes certainty over production figures impossible. However, the general picture is clear and is summarised in table 2.3.[16]

Flower class corvettes saw extensive service with the RCN.[17] Under the 1939–40 programme,

sixty-four ships were ordered in January 1940, the first fourteen to Admiralty specification. Six similar ships were ordered under the 1940–1 programme. Under the same programme, ten Modified Flowers were ordered, with increased sheer and flare, and a long forecastle. The fifteen and twelve ships ordered in 1942–3 and 1943–4 respectively had the same features but more rake to the stem and, most importantly, endurance increased to 7,400 miles at 10 knots.

A total of twenty-two ships were ordered for the French navy. Six were ordered from French yards, of which two were broken up on the stocks after the German invasion. The remaining four were completed as German patrol boats PA1–4. All were sunk and they played no part in the Battle of the Atlantic. Six were ordered from Harland and Wolff and were reordered for the RN as part of the 8 April 1940 order. Of the Smith's Dock six, one, *La Bastiaise*, was mined on trials. This was a special tragedy as the engineer manager of Smith's Dock and several of his staff went down with the ship. Later, in 1941–2, eight British-built Flowers were transferred to the Forces Navales Françaises Libres. Arguments over payment for the French

Clematis. This view shows the open well deck in front of the bridge making passage wet.

Table 2.3: British Flower class orders

Date	Number	Notes
26 July 1939	26	1939–40 Estimates
31 August 1939	30	These two orders went to seventeen small yards not normally warship builders
19 September 1939	20	All Harland & Wolff
21 September 1939	10	Small yards
12 December 1939	10	Small yards
15 December 1939	19	Small yards
8 April 1940	14	Small yards
Rest of 1940	11	Small yards (three had River names originally)
1941	2	One reordered as Castle
1942	7	

Below: Trillium shows the appearance of most Flowers by 1942.

Bottom: Asphodel in 1943 shows the features of most RN early Flowers by that date: the standard bridge with Type 271 radar and Oerlikons.

ships continued for a long while.

When the US entered the war in December 1941, they found that the USN was very short of escorts, and ten RN corvettes were transferred as PG62–71. Fifteen more building in Canada were allocated to the USN, though they finally took only eight, numbers between PG86 and PG96, the other seven coming to the RN. In the ex-RN ships a US 4in replaced the British gun, and a 3in the pom-pom. The Canadian-built ships mounted two 3in AA.

Problems, Real and Imaginary
'Moral is, don't try and force cheap ships on

Mahratta (ex-*Charlock*), a modified Flower with increased sheer and flare. The funnel is vertical and the conspicuous ventilators of the earlier ships are missing, showing that she has forced-draught boilers.

the Navy, which as Winston says, "always travels first class".' [18]

The entry of the first ships into service from April 1940 brought many complaints. Some were well justified but others arose from the RN's lack of familiarity with small ships in a seaway. As discussed above, they were intended to have two big masts. The after mast was omitted after six British-built ships, but about fifty Canadian vessels received two masts. The big foremast in front of the bridge was a serious obstruction to the important view ahead. In most, the mast was resited when the bridge was

rebuilt in 1941. *Gladiolus* was the first, completing on 6 April. She was to have a short but exciting life. She sank U-26 on 1 July 1940 and U-65 on 28 April 1941. After several other encounters she was herself sunk, probably by U-553, on 17 October 1941.

The original complement proposed was an unrealistic twenty-nine but by the time they entered the Western Approaches they carried a total of forty-seven. Additional equipment and the need for continuous watchkeeping brought further increases, and by January 1941 *Asphodel* had a complement of sixty-seven men. The first fifty ships had no thermal insulation on the ship's

Trentonian, a Canadian modified Flower.

Arbutus, a modified Flower; note the raised Hedgehog.

side and this, combined with poor ventilation, led to heavy condensation, which together with leaky seams contributed to a high incidence of tuberculosis. Seven POs shared a toilet and three washbasins. The ratings' quarters measured about twenty-two feet by thirty feet for fifty-five men, with a single urinal, two toilets and four wash bowls. Sleeping quarters were in two compartments of twenty feet by fourteen feet on the lower deck, making escape difficult (see escape, chapter 8).

There was a single, small galley at the after end of the superstructure and all food had to be carried across the open well deck, frequently swept by heavy seas, to the forecastle. There was a single, small refrigerator. Fresh food would be gone in about five days, after which only tinned supplies were available. Seasickness reduced the need for eating.

A considerable improvement was made by extending the forecastle to amidships in 1941–2. This helped to keep the deck dry and made extra space available for accommodation. There was a slight offset in that the extra weight forward reduced the freeboard.

It is a truism that small ships are more lively in a seaway than are their bigger sisters; indeed more recent work has shown that seasickness is almost a function of the length of the vessel. The original Flowers rolled badly, partly due to inadequate bilge keels (see table 2.4). Rolling particularly affects manual tasks

such as reloading depth charge throwers and other weapons. A frequent comment was that a Flower would roll on wet grass. Bigger bilge keels helped to some extent but these small ships when encountering big seas were forced to roll in the period at which they encountered the waves.

Bridge layout was, and still is, a matter of considerable debate amongst seamen, with varied and often conflicting views. The one thing that RN officers were agreed on was that the bridge should be open and, with 30–50 per cent of first sightings made visually up to the end of 1942, they were surely right (though the USN preferred enclosed bridges). It was generally believed at the time that plenty of cold, fresh air helped to keep lookouts and the officer of the watch awake. Post-war research shows that cold is likely to reduce alertness.

The original bridge design incorporated an enclosed wheelhouse, which also contained the asdic display. Changes were soon made, at first on an ad hoc basis but the introduction of radar meant that another office was needed, close to the aerial. It was also decided to fit machine guns in the bridge wings, later changed to single Oerlikons, which had to be extended to give the guns a decent arc of fire and to keep their moving, ferrous mass away from the magnetic compass. This led to a standardised bridge design fitted in almost all ships at the same time as the forecastle was extended. The package update,

Table 2.4: Flower Class Rolling[19]

Ship	Wind force	Sea	Swell	Amplitude out–out (°)	Full period (secs)	GM (feet)
Heather	7–8	5	3	17	4.8–8.4	2.6
Salvia	4	3	2	16	6.5–8.4	2.4

comprising bridge and forecastle extensions, Hedgehog and asdic 144, took about fifteen weeks.

At the front of the bridge there was an overhanging box containing the asdic and a small chart room. The compass was raised behind. The bridge was the full width of the ship, with a single Oerlikon either side (later replaced by a 6pdr in some ships). At the back was the radar office for the Type 271, with its lantern above. A few ships had this on the centreline but in most it was offset to port to improve the view aft. The wheelhouse was found to obstruct the view for visual signalling, so important before TBS, and the wheel was moved below. A few ships had a similar bridge adapted for a short forecastle.

The 4in gun was mounted on the forecastle on a low platform. Even this allowed insufficient depression for close range shots over the bow and the gun was raised further in the Modified Flowers, which involved raising the bridge. Later

in the war, two more single Oerlikons were added each side in the waist. A few ships had the pom-pom replaced by a power-operated twin Oerlikon.

Some corvettes had radar 286M (fixed) or 286P (rotating). These were useful for station-keeping but not very effective against submarines. Early Canadian ships had SW-1 and 2, of generally similar performance. At the end of March 1941 the first 271 set underwent trials in *Orchis*. This was a giant leap forward, particularly when fitted with PPI.

Initially, Flowers had twenty-five depth charges with two rails and two throwers. This was soon increased to forty charges, and later, two more throwers were added. The original asdic was type 123 (trawler dome, ie non-retractable) In 1942–3 a split Hedgehog was fitted behind the 4in gun, with twelve spigots either side of the ship.

In later ships, the hull form was modified, with increased flare and sheer. The 4in gun was

Burnet, a modified Flower, unusual in having a tripod mast.

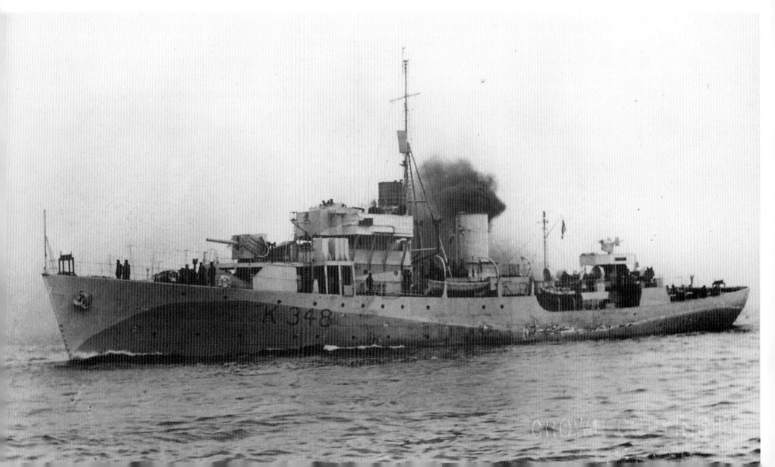

raised to fire at depression over the raised bow, which, in turn, meant raising the bridge by one deck. Most, though not all, of these Modified Flower class had a short mainmast. They had water-tube boilers with forced draught through a closed stokehold. This eliminated the 'trademark' four cowl ventilators of the earlier ships. The funnel was vertical with a cinder screen (on most) to make it more difficult to determine the course. There were twenty-two UK built ships and about thirty-seven in Canada. There were some intermediate ships with some of these features only. The Flower class ships could be built on the Great Lakes.

Modifications to RCN ships followed the same pattern as the RN's, but distance from the supplier usually meant that modifications came much later in the Canadian ships.

The A–I Class Destroyers – Excellence to Obsolescence

At the end of the first world war the V&W classes of destroyers were the best destroyers in the world, at least for a North Sea war: seaworthy, well armed and with adequate endurance. There were a considerable number of these ships available – more than enough for the peacetime fleet – so there was no urgency in the need for new designs.[20]

By November 1923, agreement had been reached on outline requirements for a new destroyer; it was very much a 'W Mk II'. DNC's destroyer section under C J W Hopkins prepared three sketch designs around these requirements and these were shown to five leading destroyer builders, who were invited to use their expertise in developing the best future destroyer. Designs by Thornycroft and Yarrow were preferred and orders were placed with them for *Ambuscade* (Yarrow) and *Amazon* (Thornycroft). As usual, Yarrow had gone for light weight, whilst Thornycroft's design was bigger and more powerful.

In the late summer of 1926, before the two prototypes completed, requirements were drawn up for the A class of eight destroyers and a rather bigger leader. They were designed by DNC's destroyer section, though some features of the Thornycroft design were incorporated. These destroyers were generally well liked, though there was a widespread view in the Royal Navy that they were too big, too complicated and too expensive, while at the same time much extra equipment was proposed. Many similar ships followed, with a total of seventy-nine ships for the RN and RCN up to the I class. In addition, at the outbreak of war there were eight similar ships building in the UK for other countries (six

Last of the line: HMCS *Sackville*, preserved at Halifax, Nova Scotia.

Table 2.4: A and I class destroyer specifications (as built)

	A class	I class
Displacement (tons):	1,330, 1,738 deep	1,450, 1,877 deep (typical)
Dimensions (feet):	323 x 32¼ x 10¼	323 x 33 x 12½
Shp and speed (kts):	34,000 = 35.25	34,000 = 36
Fuel (tons), endurance (miles) @ (kts):	390, 4,650 @ 15	450, 5,300 @ 15
Complement:	138	145
Cost:	~ £250,000	~ £250,000

H class for Brazil and two I class for Turkey), which were taken over.

All these vessels were planned as fleet destroyers, with torpedo attack on the enemy battle fleet as their primary task, together with frustrating attacks by enemy destroyers on their own fleet. Initially, the intention was that alternate flotillas would have asdic, and the others would have the two-speed destroyer sweep (TSDS) instead. The As were intended to have asdic but there was no production set available and they completed without, although they did receive their asdic sets before the war. The Bs were fitted on build, and from the D class onwards asdic was fitted to all during build. It

was said that fitting asdic added £2,500 to the quarter of a million pounds that the vessels cost.

Even in their designed role, these ships had a number of weaknesses, most of which were recognised at the time but could not be cured within the budget or technology available. There was a demand for greater endurance, met in part by more oil, but this made the ship bigger and more expensive. The machinery of the new ships was more efficient than that of the wartime destroyers, mainly as a result of the use of super-heaters, but also because of better materials. A further improvement was attempted in the *Acheron* with the use of steam at a much higher temperature and pressure (700°F and 500lb/in^2

Brilliant in 1943 with a typical destroyer fit for that date. She has lost Y gun but has Hedgehog, extra depth charges, radar, HF/DF and Oerlikons.

in *Acheron*, 300lb/in² in the rest; cf the contemporary USS *Mahan*, 700°, 400lb/in²). This plant in *Acheron* was successful in improving efficiency, with a fuel consumption of 0.608lb/shp/hr compared with a figure of 0.81 for her sisters. However, *Acheron*'s machinery gave a lot of trouble, which was never cured. The main problem lay in vibration of the blades in the impulse stage of her Parsons turbines. US sources say that the Parsons design team of this era were very old fashioned and had neglected recent work on blade flutter.[21] By the late 1930s, USN machinery was some 20–30 per cent better in fuel economy, lighter and more compact, and required much less maintenance.

There were a few experimental boilers but no significant improvement was shown. All these ships had three boilers, so that they could keep up with the fleet using two only while one was being cleaned or otherwise maintained. By the outbreak of war, RN boilers needed cleaning every 750 running hours (cf USN, 2,000 hours), which fitted in well with the peacetime leave routine. In the earlier ships, the three boilers were in two rooms: two boilers in the forward space, one aft. This meant that it was easy to immobilise the ship with a hit anywhere in the machinery.[22] There was a slight improvement from the E class onwards, with three boiler rooms. A unit system (ie with two engine rooms) would have made the ship ten feet longer and cost an extra £15,000.

Another well-known problem was that the 4.7in guns were low angle only and had no capability against closing aircraft. Many attempts were made to give at least one gun a 60° elevation but no success was achieved. The problem was that high angles of elevation needed high trunnions, but this would make the gun very difficult to load at low angles. It may be concluded that a hand-loaded, dual-purpose gun was not feasible and that power operation was needed. Since the RAF advised that dive-bombing was not a serious threat and that high-level bombers could not hit a manoeuvring destroyer, the lack of an AA gun was not seen as too serious. The low-angle guns could protect the battle line in barrage fire, though the RN AA control system was poor.

The ships were constructed of D-quality steel, riveted, with transverse frames. Stresses were reasonable for this style of construction. The single-riveted seams, particularly on the forecastle deck, were very prone to leaking. The weight saving achieved by the use of D-quality was not great; this was studied in the design of the Hunt class, where a saving of thirteen tons was estimated. D-quality was difficult to weld and other navies that welded similar steels had many problems. However, it is probable that a bigger weight saving would have been obtained by adopting a welded, mild-steel structure. Some welding was introduced with the H class.

Table 2.5: Design stresses in the I class		
	Hogging (tons/in²)	Sagging (tons/in²)
Keel	6.2	5.7
Deck	8.3	5.5

Intact stability was satisfactory, with a GM of 2.4 feet (light), 2.25 feet (deep) in the I class. They were expected to have a slight positive GM with the engine room and adjacent boiler room flooded. This is far below modern standards but was adequate, since only six capsized after a single torpedo hit; twenty-two broke in half. None were lost to the stress of weather alone. For some reason unknown, *Duncan* had two boilers in the room next to the engine room, making her liable to a great flooded length if hit in this region.

By 1941, weight growth was a serious problem, with 100–150 tons additional weight for radar, HF/DF, Oerlikons, splinter protection and depth charges – the heavy Mk VII was a particular problem. Too many coats of paint were another load, particularly on the leaders, which always looked immaculate. Some three to four inches of metacentric height had been lost out of an initial thirty inches in the light condition. Most had a fuel restriction imposed, requiring them to take in water ballast if fuel fell below forty tons – a further restriction on endurance. This restriction was generally ignored to save the effort needed to clean the tanks before refuelling.

The initial main armament was eight 21in torpedo tubes in quadruple mounts (ten in the I class). In the real war, these were often known as the 'main ornament'. There were four 4.7in QF guns (five in most leaders) and two single pom-poms. They had two depth charge throwers and four chutes with, initially, eight charges (increased to fifteen by the outbreak of war). They all had asdic 128 by 1939.

During the war A–I class ships were gradually replaced on fleet duties by later vessels and relegated to 'secondary' duties such as ASW. The A and B classes were already available for such work at the start of the war. Initial changes were few; the after set of torpedo tubes was replaced by a 3in AA gun, which, without control, was useless. The number of depth charges was increased with, in most cases, the loss of Y gun. Oerlikons were added as they became available, with six in most survivors by 1944.

Some ships were given a more specific ASW fit, with A gun replaced by Hedgehog with asdic 144 plus Q (see appendix IV). The number of depth charges steadily increased, with 35 in early war years rising to between 60 and 135 in some ships with four throwers. *Ambuscade* was a test bed for Parsnip[23] and later for Squid. *Escapade* had a serious explosion in her Hedgehog and was given Squid during repairs.

As escorts, their virtue was their speed and they were often used to pursue a contact, accounting for a high proportion of 'kills' in the early years. On the other hand, their endurance was insufficient to escort a convoy across the Atlantic. Refuelling at sea was only a partial answer, as the techniques and equipment available were time-consuming and could be used only in good weather. Some consideration was given in September 1943 to a long-range escort conversion. This would have been difficult, as almost all had two boilers in the forward room, which would have meant an extra oil-tight bulkhead for the new tank.

It is interesting that the conversion package would have included strengthening by doublers on the upper deck and thicker garboard strakes – incidentally reducing the ballast needed! The overall strength of these ships appears to have been satisfactory but wave impacts and slamming led to leaky single-riveted seams, which were unpleasant in mess decks and potentially disastrous in feed-water tanks. The break of forecastle amidships formed a structural discontinuity, which led many to break in half after damage.

Their low freeboard to the upper deck made its passage hazardous in bad weather and reloading depth charges was particularly dangerous. Their turning circle was on the wide side for depth charge attacks but overall they were effective ASW vessels of their day, participating in thirty-nine sinkings.

Hurricane as leader of B1 Escort Group with a similar ASW fit to *Brilliant*.

3
After the Fall of France:
June 1940–March 1941

The fall of France altered the whole geography of the battle. U-boats operating from Lorient and other French ports were many miles – days – nearer their operational station, so that their operational time was much increased. On the day after the French armistice, a train left for France carrying fuel, weapons, provisions, spares and maintenance personnel. On 3 July U-30 entered Lorient to embark fuel and new torpedoes. It is not easy to estimate the benefit of time on station; there was a concealed advantage, as much of the old route from German North Sea bases had to be traversed submerged for fear of attack. Hessler has estimated that the overall effect was about a week (25 per cent) extra on station per sortie. Kessler notes that before the fall of France, U-boat Command needed 2.35 boats in maintenance for each one on operations.[1] When the French ports became available, this ratio changed to 1.84 to 1, a 22 per cent improvement.

The use of the French bases eased the maintenance load and it was even said that French workers were better than the Germans at home. In the north, Norwegian ports brought the north-western approaches within range of the small Type II boats. There was a very small offset with the British occupation of Iceland, though it was early 1941 before the RAF had aircraft available to base there.

The advance of the German armies posed other problems for the Royal Navy. Many destroyers and escorts had been sunk or damaged during the Dunkirk operation and other evacuations, and repairs take time.

Additionally, a considerable number of the best destroyers were held in south- and east-coast ports as part of the protection against a possible invasion. In July the Nore command alone had thirty-two modern destroyers and five corvettes, while more were held on the south coast. Only in September did the Defence Committee under the chairmanship of the prime minister agree that the threat of defeat in the Atlantic was greater than that of invasion and release the destroyers to the Western Approaches. The English Channel was closed to ocean shipping and all convoys were routed to the north of Ireland. The shortage of escorts was so severe that most convoys in June and July had only a single escort for much of the way.

In June 1940 U-boat Command had only fifty-one U-boats available, six fewer than at the outbreak of war, and many were undergoing refit or repair following the Norwegian campaign. Considerable progress had been made in rectifying the torpedo problems. By 9 June sixteen boats were assembled in the Western Approaches, and Dönitz planned wolf-pack attacks on convoys HX48 and WS3. Fortunately, his intelligence was incorrect and contact was not made. The German B-Dienst had broken the RN administrative code before the war, which gave general information on the sailing of convoys. Only in August did the Admiralty change to a more difficult code. Dönitz also hoped to rely on aircraft sightings. The first choice was the He 177 but the early examples were so prone to set themselves on fire that they were not used over the sea. The replacement was

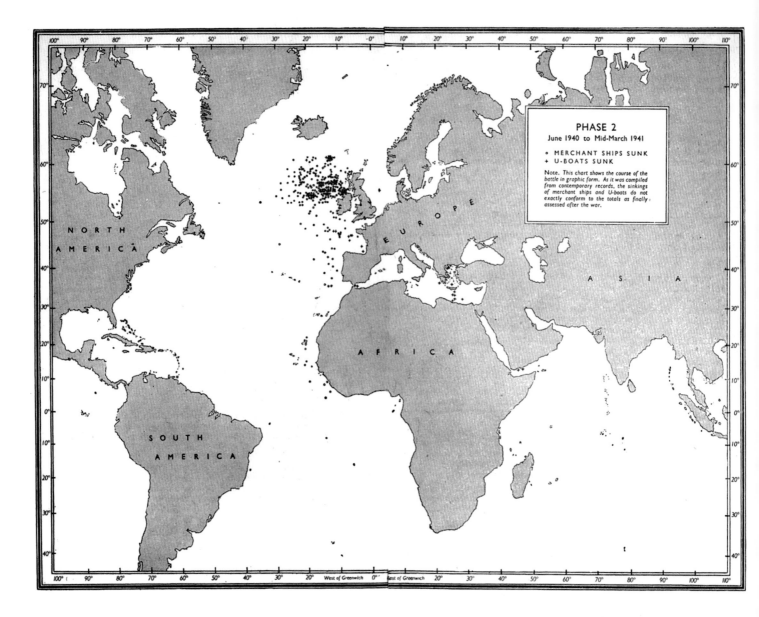

PHASE 2
June 1940 to Mid-March 1941
• MERCHANT SHIPS SUNK
+ U-BOATS SUNK

Note. This chart shows the course of the
battle in graphic form. As it was compiled
from contemporary records, the sinkings
of merchant ships and U-boats do not
exactly conform to the totals as finally
assessed after the war.

Phase 2 of the Atlantic battle. With the fall of France homeward bound traffic was routed through the north-west approaches, to the north of Ireland. Escorts were very weak both in ships and aircraft and U-boat attacks were concentrated in these approaches. A small number of attacks occurred off the West African coast.

the FW 200 Condor, an adapted passenger airliner. It too, was unreliable, as the tail would fall off in violent manoeuvres, but it was still a useful, even formidable, opponent.

Further attempts at wolf-pack attacks in August were largely ruined by bad weather but Dönitz interpreted the results as showing that he was working on the right lines. Then on 21/22 September five boats concentrated on convoy HX72, which had been sighted by U-47 following a signal interception by B-Dienst. In a series of attacks, eleven merchant ships of 73,000 tons were sunk. In mid-October two further attacks on convoys SC7 and HX79 confirmed Dönitz's tactics. Some names that were all too

well known already came to the fore: Kretschmer, Prien, Endrass and Schepke.

Monthly sinkings were well over 200,000 tons per month, up to 360,000 in June and October 1940. Viewed another way, the figures looked even worse; there were only about ten to twelve U-boats at sea at any one time and they were averaging 500–1,000 tons sunk *per day* each. The number of U-boats training or new boats working up had risen from twenty-four in June 1940 to eighty-two in March 1941. Clearly, worse was to come. There was very little to look forward to; as the USA was still neutral, there was no vast stream of new merchant ships and escorts coming from them as in 1918. There was no active assistance in anti-submarine work from the USN. Canada's contribution to both merchant-ship and escort building was already becoming significant. It was perhaps the darkest hour of the battle, without a light at the end of the tunnel.

Available escorts were much as in the previous phase, though Flower class corvettes began to operate. *Gladiolus* was the first to complete and, appropriately, she was the first to score, sinking U-26 (with RAAF assistance) on 3 July 1940. *Rhododendron* scored on 21 November and *Arbutus* with *Camellia* accounted for U-47 on 7 March 1941. Altogether, fifteen U-boats were sunk from June 1940 to March 1941. Most of the surface-ship kills were with depth charge, though, unusually, *Walker* torpedoed U-99 and *Vanoc* rammed U-100. Even when there were several escorts to a convoy, they had rarely operated together and co-ordinated counter-attacks were almost impossible with the primitive signalling devices available. The fifty ex-USN flush-deck destroyers began to operate towards the end of the period.

Table 3.1: Causes of U-boat sinkings, June 1940–March 1941	
Surface vessels	8½
Aircraft	½
Submarine	1
Mines	1
Accident and unknown	4

Almost all of the sinkings by surface ships were due to convoy escorts.

Technical and Other Developments

There were a number of developments in technology, training and other areas during this period for which Dunbar-Nasmith deserves credit. Few were of operational significance at the time but they contributed a great deal to the 'gleam of light' described in the next chapter.

Early Radar

Although the Admiralty was involved in the development of radar (known as RDF until June 1943) almost from its conception in 1935,

Mansfield in 1942 is fairly typical of the ex-American Town class. She has one US 4in gun and a British 12pdr aft. Although less than ideal as ASW ships, the fifty old destroyers acquired under the Lend-lease agreement were a welcome reinforcement when they entered service at the beginning of 1941.

resources were very limited and progress was slow.[2] What effort was made available was concentrated on air warning sets, and by 1938 *Rodney* and *Sheffield* had early development units of Type 79. This was a very successful set and remained in service well after the war. Fire-control radars came second.

After the fall of France a requirement was formulated for a surface set to detect surfaced submarines or invasion craft. A test had been carried out some time earlier with a 1.5-metre ASV Mk I radar fitted to a Walrus aircraft standing on the slipway at Lee on Solent. It was capable of detecting ships at a distance of five miles. The decision to proceed was taken in early June and an aerial suitable for a small ship's mast was made in little over a week. This came into naval service as the Type 286. The aerial was fixed pointing forward and the ship had to be turned to sweep a wider arc. The first sea trials took place with *Verity* on 19 June 1940. Only a few ships were fitted with the basic 286, which was superseded by the 286M, based around the better-engineered ASV Mk II. This still used the fixed aerial and also suffered from extensive side lobes, which were particularly confusing with the multiple echoes obtained from a convoy. It was not very effective at picking up submarines but made an enormous difference to station-keeping at night.

By March 1941, some ninety escorts had 286M. It covered an arc from the bow to just abaft the beam on either side. The simple aerial was quite heavy and several ships broke their masts when rolling heavily; *Sardonyx* broke hers in July 1941 and again two months later. The first success, and a very important one, came on 17 March 1941, when *Vanoc* detected and killed U-100, along with her commander, the ace, Schepke (see chapter 4). It was probably the only sinking directly attributable to a 286 with fixed aerial, though there were other contacts.

Canada developed a home-grown radar set, SW-1 (and the later SW-2), which was comparable with 286 but even less reliable. A more valuable Canadian contribution was in the supply of physics graduates who were trained as radar officers (sub-lieutenant) and lent to the RN. RDF ratings were not trained to maintain their sets in the early days. The Royal Australian Navy also contributed a number of officers and men.

Code Breaking[3]

By the mid-1930s, there was a general awareness in all navies of the part played by Signals Intelligence (SIGINT) in the submarine campaign of World War I and most took some steps to prepare for similar activities. There are three main types of SIGINT, although these may overlap. First comes full deciphering of enemy signals, preferably quickly enough for the intelligence to be used in current operations. Second is the location of a transmitter by direction finding. Finally, it may be possible to recognise a pattern in messages and their sequel, eg a message from a minesweeper followed by the passage of a high-value unit may be recognised as an 'all clear'.

Simple precautions include minimising the use of radio and keeping messages very short. Codes were supposed to be changed frequently; a common error was to transmit the same text in both the new code and, for the benefit of ships which had not received the new code, a transmission in the old code. There was the eternal problem that operational use of intelligence will often disclose the source.

Before the war, the German B-Dienst had made considerable progress in breaking both the code and the super-enciphering of the British Naval Cipher No. 1 and the Naval Code. In the opening months the RN use of radio was limited and the Germans had little advantage from their achievement. During the confusion of the Norwegian campaign, however, radio was used to a greater extent and Germany gained from the ability to read messages.

After the fall of France, U-boat Command were able to read convoy-routing signals in slow time but the format of the signal indicated the pattern of movement. This would change in the next phase.

Rescue

Traditionally, sailors have always given high priority to rescue and, initially, it was hoped that this approach would be sufficient in the convoy war. The last ship in each column was supposed to stop and rescue survivors if any ship ahead was sunk. There were a number of problems; with eastbound convoys, all ships carried valuable cargoes, which would be put at risk,

The quarter view of *Mansfield* illustrates some of the problems of the class. The very fine stern lines needed very large guards to protect the big propellers, and the quarterdeck was too small for an extensive depth charge fit.

together with the ship itself and its crew, if it stopped in the vicinity of a submarine. There was a different problem with ships in westbound convoys, as most ships were in ballast, lightly loaded, with high freeboard, making them hard to steer, so that rescue was physically difficult as well as hazardous. Many rescues were carried out by escorts, which not only exposed them to risk but reduced the already inadequate number of vessels on the screen.

The weakness of this approach was apparent as losses mounted after the fall of France. The loss of crews was as serious as that of ships. The training of both officers and men was lengthy and hence the pool of seamen was limited. It was also realised that morale would suffer unless it was known that survivors could be confident of a speedy rescue. At the end of September 1940, C-in-C Western Approaches drew the attention of the Admiralty to these problems and suggested special rescue ships. Action was rapid and the first such ship, *Beachy*, sailed on 9 October.

The ships chosen were mainly passenger/cargo vessels operating in the UK coastal trade. They were usually of about 1,500grt and 250 feet in length.[4] They had merchant ship crews and flew the RFA blue ensign with the Admiralty anchor. It was thought that their small size would reduce the risk of attack, while their low freeboard would facilitate the actual task of rescue. The degree of alteration increased as time went by. Most were ballasted to their normal deep draught and many had empty drums stowed in their holds to maintain buoyancy and stability in the event of flooding. Fuel stowage was increased, often involving extra bulkheads, to enable a passage across the Atlantic without refuelling. There were also five Castle class corvettes, converted while building, and bearing 'Empire' names. They only entered service in late 1944 and played little part in operations.

Eventually, most could accommodate thirty officer survivors in two-berth cabins and 150 seamen in bunk spaces. Extra washplaces and toilets were installed and catering facilities were increased. A specially designed rescue boat was fitted on either beam. A properly fitted sick bay and operating theatre with an RN surgeon and sick berth attendant came a little later in the war, making them invaluable to treat minor injuries and illnesses within the 2,500–10,000 men of the convoy. They had a fairly full communications fit, with a team of RN operators, and carried HF/DF gear. Their station at the rear of the convoy made them invaluable in the sheepdog role. About thirty rescue ships entered service, of which five were lost to enemy action and one, probably, as a result of icing.

Personal survival gear was either lacking or deficient. An inflatable life jacket had been tested in 1939 and found to be dangerous, as it tipped the head of an unconscious man under water, but it remained in production throughout the war. There were no survival suits, so life in cold water was brief. The main vehicle for survivors was the Carley float, with a buoyant ring supporting a grating on which survivors sat, half immersed in the sea. Even this crude device doubled the chance of survival in the sea. It was easy to launch and in most installations would float off a sinking ship. No real thought had been given to the means of getting survivors from the sea or a raft into a rescue ship. After the war, the Talbot Committee concluded that the majority of those lost at sea in the RN had escaped from their sinking ship and died in the water. They found that no department of the Admiralty was responsible for survival aids. The merchant service was probably even worse off, relying on traditional kapok or cork jackets and totally exposed rafts.

Training

Training was a major factor in the Battle of the Atlantic. The best of tools is of little value if the operator is lacking in skill. The majority of officers and ratings were 'Hostilities Only', with little if any seagoing experience; indeed some, particularly Canadian, had never seen the sea. Training can be divided into three levels, though there was some overlap: basic equipment, ship and unit.[5] It is notable that the most successful commanders insisted in spending considerable time when in harbour in practising the basic tasks, such as reloading depth charge throwers.

The benefit of plenty of such practice loadings made it a little less difficult to load at night with the ship rolling and heaving while covered in spray if not green seas.

In early 1940 the Admiralty decided that a training base should be set up to train whole ships' crews in the latest techniques and provide refresher courses. The site chosen was Lorient as a joint RN–FN base, but little had been done by the time of the fall of France – except for the appointment of Vice Adm (retired) Gilbert Stephenson in the rank of commodore.

A new site was chosen, at Tobermory, and it was operational by July 1940. The first headquarters/accommodation ship was a decrepit ex-yacht dating from 1891, renamed *Western Isles*, requisitioned in April 1940 and converted by Barclay Curle on the Clyde. She was renamed *Eastern Isles* in October 1941, the role of HQ ship being taken by a more up-to-date *Western Isles* (ex-*Batavier IV*) dating from 1902. The dates are significant, as they show the early recognition of the importance of training by the Admiralty. *Western Isles* only went to sea once – to qualify for duty-free drinks.

The syllabus varied from class to class, depending on the complexity of their equipment, but the course was usually two to three weeks. The role had changed significantly and concentrated on the work-up of newly commissioned ships rather than the original concept of a refresher course. The emphasis was on urgency and the unexpected; the commodore would often board a new arrival before mooring was complete and proclaim that the ship was on fire or that there was a man overboard. For many, this was their first ship and they were not long in uniform. Cdre Stephenson found that a short but tough period of close-order drill was useful.

Every weapon and sensor was exercised and there was a real, albeit ancient, submarine with which to exercise. Hours were long, though sleeping hours were usually undisturbed – except for teasing the sentries. The final reports exposed every weakness, with an ultimate sanction of repeating the course, rarely employed. Officers who did not meet the standards were removed. Twenty to twenty-five ships could work up at any one time. It was no wonder that Stephenson

Table 3.2: Flush-deck destroyers				
Class (Group)	*Burnham* (Group A)	*Montgomery* (Group B)	*Newport* (Group C)	*Leeds* (Group D)
Displacement (tons):	1,190, 1,725 deep	1,090, 1,530 deep	1,060, 1,530 deep	1,020, 1,445 deep
Dimensions (feet):	314¼ x 31¾ x 17¾	314¼ x 31 x 12	314¼ x 31¾ x 12	315½ x 31¼ x 11
Shp and speed (kts):	27,000 = 28.5	ca. 25,000 = 28	ca. 26,000 = 27.75	18,500 = 30[6]
Fuel (tons), endurance (miles) @ (kts):	375, 3,425 @ 15	275, 2,800 @ 15	275, 2,250 @ 15	205, 2,250 @ 15
Complement (original): ~150				
Leeds, Ludlow 3-shaft ungeared, rest 2-shaft geared turbines				

became known as the 'Terror of Tobermory'. He worked up his thousandth ship in October 1944, drawing the inevitable comparison with Helen of Troy. Perhaps the greatest tribute to Cdre Stephenson is that the current work-up training for the RN is closely modelled on his plan at Tobermory. This RN course attracts ships from many other navies. Tobermory was overloaded and a similar establishment, HMS *Mentor*, was opened at Stornoway in December 1943, but closed when the rate of completion of new escorts dropped off. Another base was set up in Bermuda for the use of frigates built in the USA. Capacity was limited to twelve because of the need to provide sheltered berths during hurricanes.

The Towns

The Town class were sometimes referred to as 'flush deckers', which was a correct description of their profile, or alternatively 'four stackers', which was incorrect since two of the fifty ships

transferred to the RN were built with three funnels and others were altered with two or three. As built at the end of World War I, they fell into four main groups, though there were variations between ships of a group.

Negotiations to obtain destroyers from the USN began with the fall of France, and an agreement was signed on 3 September 1940 to transfer fifty ships in exchange for the lease of bases in the West Indies. A considerable amount of preparatory work must have been completed, as the first eight ships arrived in Halifax, Nova Scotia on 7 September. It was originally intended to retain the US names, and this batch were commissioned as 'HMS', followed by the US name, on 9 September. The decision to give them new names based on places in the USA and UK that shared the same name was made on the 19th, but not implemented until 2 October. In the meantime a second batch of seven ships had commissioned with their original names.[7]

Leeds, one of a pair of three-funnelled Group D Towns. They did not take part in the Atlantic battle but were employed almost exclusively on east coast duties.

Churchill is similar in configuration to *Mansfield*.

Rockingham was refitted at Devonport from December 1940 to February 1941 and served in the Western Approaches until a refit at Southampton from May to August 1941. She became an air target ship in December 1943 and sank on a British mine in September 1944.

On arrival in Halifax, the British or Canadian crew joined with the US crews for two days, learning how everything worked. An inspection led to a critical but helpful report. Hull and main machinery was generally in good condition, but auxiliaries, piping and wiring were in poor shape.

Two major problems soon became apparent.

Brighton completed her refit in January 1941 and served in the Atlantic. She was badly damaged in collision with the cruiser *Kenya* in June 1941 and following another collision was laid up. She was lent to Russia in 1944 and scrapped on return.

Corroded rivets in the shell plating allowed sea water to enter the fuel tanks causing, in the worst cases, complete loss of power. A temporary cure was found by carefully cleaning the tank and refilling with clean oil but the problem would recur for the rest of their short service lives. Another long-term problem was due to the operation of the rudder by long runs of wires and chains from the steering wheel. These would break or jam at critical moments, losing steering.[8] In RN service it was found necessary to change all this gear every three months. Their turning circle of 770 yards at fifteen knots was nearly twice that of an RN destroyer.

The hull form had been successfully optimised for minimum resistance in still water, with very fine ends. At the after end, this led to a tiny quarterdeck, which made difficult the installation and operation of depth charge gear, while the big propellers projected far beyond the ship's side and were easily damaged, particularly during frequent steering failures. At the other end, the freeboard was low because the sheer was insufficient to make up for the lack of a forecastle and hence the shipping of green seas was all too common. The bridge was well forward and easily damaged, while several ships also lost funnels. Forward of the gun, there was a large access hatch to the mess deck which was also liable to damage.

In the USN, the ship was controlled from an enclosed bridge with only a lookout platform above. The US 4in gun was criticised, mainly because of the flimsy nature of its fixed ammunition. The 3in AA gun had an elevation of 75° but could not be used at angles greater than 40°. As transferred, they mounted two triple 21in torpedo tubes on either beam but this was not a great success as the outboard ends of the tubes would dip into the water during a turn. The torpedoes were unreliable and ran some ten feet deeper than the setting.

Of the fifty ships, six commissioned with Canadian crews and, initially, the remainder with British. Australia and New Zealand were asked but did not have crews to spare. Later, several were operated by Allied navies, including a dozen by the Soviet Union.

The inspection report was taken very seriously and resulted in a set of Stage I modifications that were applied in varying degree to all ships, mainly at Devonport, while defects were made good. It was the spring of 1941 before most ships were operational.

The American guns were removed, with the exception of the forward one, and in some ships the beam guns remained for a short time. A British 12pdr was fitted on the after deckhouse. The after two sets of torpedo tubes were removed. To improve stability, the mainmast was removed and the foremast reduced in height. The three after funnels were lowered by several feet. Most were given fifty tons of ballast and the bilge keels were increased in depth. British depth charge throwers were installed. The asdic story was a little more complicated. Three ships had no outfit and these were given simple British sets (Type 133).[9] The other forty-seven ships had USN Type QCJ/QCL, which was comparable in performance with contemporary RN sets but slightly more powerful. However, it lacked a streamlined dome, limiting use to speeds below fifteen knots. It was also more complicated and needed more skill to operate. There was no recorder; when a British unit was installed, the outfit was reclassified as British Type 141. Some were given a streamlined dome as Type 141A.

Stage II changes were applied piecemeal in many cases, depending on operational commitments – and the defect list. Changes comprised removal of the beam 4in guns, replaced by single Oerlikons, and of the remaining US torpedo tubes, to be replaced by one triple British mount on the centre line. Radar 286 was fitted at the masthead and Type 271 on the bridge in late 1941. The command was moved to an open deck above the old bridge; configuration varied. Later (late 1942), many received a Hedgehog forward. Some carried HF/DF on a mast aft.

The depth charge fit was complicated. Ships with the basic modification had a five-pattern fit with two throwers, two rails and fifty charges (Mk VII, light). The number of charges was reduced by six in ships whose funnels had not been lowered and by a further six if the starboard boat and equipment had not been removed. Ships modified in accordance with December 1941 instructions had a ten-pattern fit with two rails, four throwers (two ready-use racks per thrower) and sixty charges (fifteen heavy and fifteen light on the upper deck and ten heavy, twenty light in the magazine). There were twenty-four depth charge carriers. The three ships of Group D were used exclusively on the east coast and had one rail, two throwers and twenty charges.

Long-range escorts

At a meeting in November 1940,[10] consideration was given to converting these ships to long-range escorts, noting that the hulls and machinery were believed to be in good condition. It was desired to obtain a speed of twenty-two knots, which would allow the two forward boilers and funnels to be removed, giving space for more fuel (eighty tons) – and feed-water, unless the evaporators could be improved. Endurance at fourteen knots would go up from 2,000 to 2,780 miles. Space would also be available for W/T and asdic offices. A stronger bridge of RN style would be built further aft. All torpedo tubes and US guns would be removed. A 4in HA/LA gun would be mounted on a bandstand with breakwater, further aft than the present A gun, and another fitted aft. Two single pom-poms and two Oerlikons would be fitted. Eight depth charge

Chesterfield has a new bridge structure but is otherwise similar. It is likely that the bridge was fitted in Hull at the end of 1942.

Clare as a long-range escort. She has a different bridge a little further aft and has lost the two forward funnels and boilers. The full conversion took eight months and does not seem to have been thought worthwhile as only two more ships had similar conversions.

throwers and two rails (eight charges each) would be installed, giving a fourteen pattern. They would carry eighty-eight charges (thirty-four heavy and sixteen light on the upper deck and eleven heavy and twenty-seven light in the magazine). Asdic and radio were to be updated. It was thought that the work would take about six months, perhaps in the USA. Optimistically, it was noted that the USN still had another 120 similar ships! Later conversions would have had a fourteen-pattern fit with seventy-eight charges, soon changed to ten-pattern.

Three ships were converted to long-range escorts, a modification that predated the V&W conversions. Conversion took about eight months, although this figure means little as all the ships were in poor condition and a great deal

of other defect work was carried out at the same time. It seems to have been concluded that conversions of the Towns were not worthwhile, as no other ships were taken in hand.

They had a short and fairly undistinguished career, participating in the sinking of eight U-boats. Most were paid off or transferred to non-operational service by late 1943. The value of these ancient ships will be discussed in chapter 10.

Ex-US Coast Guard Cutters

In the spring of 1941, ten cutters of the US Coast Guard were transferred to the RN under the Lend-Lease agreement. Strictly, they were of two different classes, but the effect on performance and appearance was negligible.[11]

In several aspects they followed merchant

The ex-US Coast Guard cutter *Fishguard*. Big, comfortable and with good endurance, they mainly operated on the UK-Freetown route.

ship practice. They were single-screw, turbo-electric, driven by an AC synchronous motor. Steam came from two boilers in a single boiler room. By warship standards their subdivision was poor, as none of the bulkheads ran continuously from top to bottom and there was very little subdivision between the weather deck and the deck below. The weather deck was of wooden planking with steel stringers and steel in the way of the guns. Their stability was suspect, though doubt has been cast on this story.[12] Ballast was fitted (thirty tons) and an oil fuel restriction of fifty tons was imposed. Their size and high freeboard made them comfortable sea boats.

Accommodation was exceptionally good, even by USN standards. The captain had a suite as well as a sea cabin and there were twenty cabins for officers and warrant officers. The wardroom even had a skylight. They had cafeteria messing with ice cream machines and drinking fountains. There were very large refrigerated spaces. Some of this luxury was lost to wartime equipment; for example, the laundry was converted to a radar office.

Table 3.3: ex-US Coast Guard Cutters	
Displacement (tons): 2,116 deep	
Dimensions (feet): 250 x 42 x 16 deep	
Shp and speed (kts): 3,000 = 16	
Fuel (tons), endurance miles @ (kts): 314, 8,000 @ 8	
Complement: 160	

Their original armament was one or two 5in guns, and changes were made as convenient. By 1945, most had one 4in HA/LA gun, one Bofors, two single pom-poms and seven Oerlikons. The ships were fitted with HF/DF and 271 radar and their anti-submarine outfit consisted of Hedgehog, four throwers with two rails (ten pattern) and 100 depth charges. Their endurance and spacious living standards made them very useful for the longer routes, such as UK–Freetown, but they were little involved in the main Battle of the Atlantic.

Lulworth, another ex-USCG cutter, in late 1943 shows few changes.

4

A Gleam of Light:
April–December 1941

From the spring of 1941, things began to improve and, while the battle was far from being won, winning became a realistic possibility. This improvement was due to a number of factors, all improving and interacting one with another. If credit is to be given, it should be to the early commanders-in-chief, Dunbar-Nasmith and Noble, who initiated the successful programmes.

There were more escorts; gone were the days of only one or two per convoy. They were better trained too, both individually and as groups. The massive Canadian effort in shipbuilding and training began to pay off, despite shortages of equipment and experienced crews. Operating bases in Iceland and Newfoundland helped in making good use of the ships. It became possible to run more fast convoys, enabling the minimum speed of independents to be raised, with a marked drop in losses. The task was eased by the fitting of early radar sets, soon followed by much-superior centimetric sets of the 271 series.

It was not all good news; there were far more U-boats in commission than before, though initially most were still in home waters working up and the actual number at sea was still low. Dönitz was able to use wolf-pack tactics with increasing success, although it was noticeable that a high proportion of successes were due to a small number of aces. As Allied measures made life more difficult for U-boats, Dönitz moved his submarines westward. This exposed the limited endurance of RN destroyers, only partly offset by primitive refuelling-at-sea techniques.

Both sides depended to an increasing extent on secure radio communications and in both cases these were much less secure than was hoped. The code breakers of B-Dienst and Bletchley Park played a more and more important part in the battle. The topics introduced here will be explored in more detail in following sections.

Numbers of Escorts

It is difficult to give the numbers of the various types of escort involved in the Battle of the Atlantic. First there is the problem of geographical limits; Gibraltar convoys are included but not those in the Arctic or South Atlantic. However, diversion of considerable numbers of U-boats to the Mediterranean in this period had an important effect on the Atlantic battle. This was not only an issue for the Germans: on the Allied side, destroyers too were frequently diverted from the main battle to other areas, particularly the Arctic. The figures below and those in later chapters are only approximate. The numbers were further reduced by the need for maintenance.

At the beginning of 1941 (figures for January 1942 in brackets) there were about 36 (73) RN and 13 (67) Canadian Flowers, together with a few sloops. In addition, there were about eighty destroyers, mainly RN but a few RCN, a number which did not change greatly over the year. These destroyers were mainly World War I veterans at the beginning of the year, but later, vessels of the A–I classes joined as they were replaced by more modern ships for fleet duties.

The increased number of escorts available in the North Atlantic made improved protection for convoys possible. A typical convoy escort might now consist of two to three destroyers and four to five corvettes. Such numbers meant that there would be a complete asdic screen ahead of the convoy, making submerged attack very difficult. Night surface attack by wolf packs was already Dönitz's preferred method, but the long summer nights reduced the opportunity for such attacks. With better protection to convoys it was possible in June 1941 to raise the minimum speed for independent sailing from thirteen to fifteen knots, with a dramatic drop in sinkings. Up to June, losses of independents were running at some 200,000 tons per month but this fell to about 50,000 tons with the change.

With more escorts available there was much more chance of keeping the ships of an escort group together and even to find time for group training, discussed later. Western Atlantic command had begun to realise the futility of detaching escorts to pursue an old and distant contact.

The numbers game was far from one-sided. By the beginning of May the total number of U-boats available had risen to 139, further increasing to 184 by August and 250 by December. The effect of this vast increase was not immediately apparent, as the new boats required extensive trials and their crews needed lengthy training. In consequence, the number of boats at sea did not rise rapidly. For the nine months from April to December 1941, the average number of U-boats at sea was only about twenty-seven and not all these were in the operational area.

The Focus Shifts Westward

At the beginning of the year, the UK-based ships escorted convoys to and from 20° west. The presence of stronger escorts made attack in the area increasingly dangerous and by February the U-boats were moving further west. This movement was limited by the US-patrolled neutrality zone. These westerly longitudes were outside the range of Condor reconnaissance aircraft and the broader spread of the ocean facilitated evasive routing, which was becoming more effective with the breaking of the Enigma code.

Even while officially neutral, the USN played an increasing role in the Atlantic war and, although this book does not cover USN operations or ships, some mention is necessary. President Roosevelt announced a Neutrality Patrol on 5 September 1939 to keep war out of the western hemisphere. This was formalised in October at a pan-American conference, with a neutral zone extending for 300 miles into the Atlantic from the coasts of North and South America. Goods purchased in the USA had to be paid for in cash and carried in the purchaser's ships. This was a great help to the Allies, as no German cargo ships were at sea. Initially, the sale of munitions was prohibited but such items were put on the same basis as any other in November 1939. British dollar funds were quickly exhausted and in March 1941 the requirement for 'cash' was removed under the Lend-Lease Act.

After the fall of France, US policy moved further towards support for the UK. The exchange of fifty old destroyers for bases is discussed in chapter 3. One of these bases, Argentia, Placentia Bay, Newfoundland, was commissioned as a USN base on 15 July 1941 and was to give invaluable support to the Atlantic battle. A staff conference in January 1941 led to a promise of US support 'short of war'. The government of Iceland agreed to the stationing of a US division there from July, and USN ships escorted convoys as far as Iceland.

Support for Germany within the USA diminished during the spring of 1941 as a result of the loss of US lives in sinkings. Then, in September 1941, the destroyer USS *Greer* was trailing a U-boat, without attacking, when U-652 fired a torpedo at her, which missed, as did *Greer*'s retaliatory depth charges. Escorting convoy SC48 on 17 October, the USS *Kearney* was torpedoed but not sunk by U-568, thanks to her unit system of machinery.[1] The first loss came on 31 October with the sinking of the USS *Reuben James*.

The actual support from the USN was quite small in the period before open war but the effect on morale in the UK of feeling that she was no longer alone was very great – yet another 'gleam of light'.

A key factor in the breaking of Enigma came as a result of the westerly deployment. Four U-boats attacked outward bound convoy OB318 on 7 May 1941 and for the next four days and

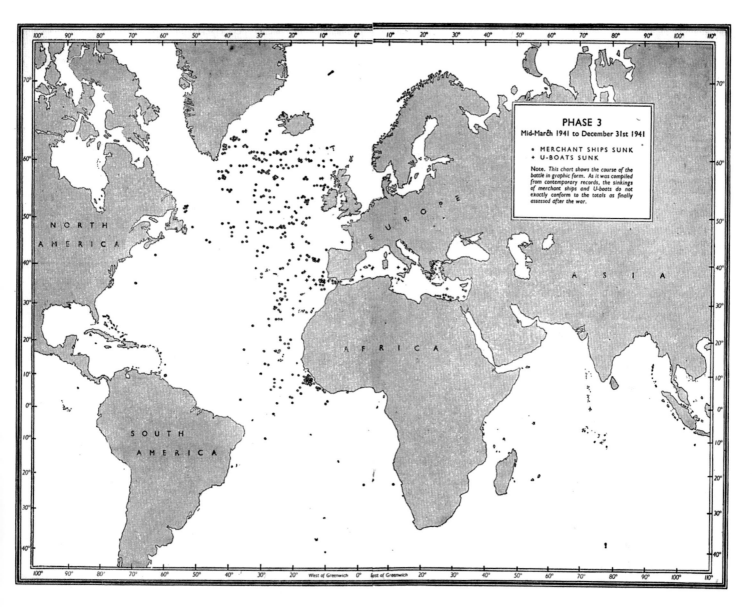

PHASE 3
Mid-March 1941 to December 31st 1941

• MERCHANT SHIPS SUNK
+ U-BOATS SUNK

Note. *This chart shows the course of the battle in graphic form. As it was compiled from contemporary records, the sinkings of merchant ships and U-boats do not exactly conform to the totals as finally assessed after the war.*

Map Phase 3. The battleground was now the whole of the Western Atlantic from the tip of Greenland to Freetown. There was still little effective air cover.

nights, sinking seven merchant ships (39,000 tons) and damaging two more. However, the depth charges of the corvette *Aubretia* and the destroyers *Broadway* and *Bulldog* brought U-110 to the surface. *Bulldog* came in to ram, but her CO decided to try to capture the submarine. A party went across in a whaler and U-110 was taken in tow. She sank, but not before her Enigma machine and code books had been removed. With justice, this has been called the most important incident of the whole battle.[2]

In August, U-570 surrendered to a Hudson aircraft. She was brought back to the UK, where much was learnt about the capability of the Type VIIC, its equipment and torpedoes. She was com-

missioned into the RN as HMS *Graph*.

The difficulty of interception with the westward spread meant that U-boats had to be arranged in long scouting lines, which, in turn, made concentration more difficult if contact was made with a convoy. In November 1940 twenty-six Italian submarines were based on Bordeaux. Dönitz did not expect much from his allies but hoped they would help in locating convoys. In fact, in five months' operations, only fourteen of the twenty-six scored any kills. Their large super-structure made them easily visible, even at night, and they were untrained in surface attacks. Their signals discipline was poor and sighting reports, even if made, often failed to get through.

After ten weeks, the attack shifted back to the east. It was hoped that the greater number of Condor aircraft would permit three flights per day and enable convoys to be located. However, it seems that there were only two examples of such location. On the other hand, the more numerous escorts enabled ships on an outer screen to locate a shadower in good time and at least force it to remain submerged and so lose contact. From mid-September to November only five convoys were attacked, losing forty-six ships totalling 198,000 tons.

Then, in November–December, twenty U-boats were detached to the Mediterranean, losing three in transiting the Straits of Gibraltar. Though they scored a few successes against naval targets (*Barham* and *Ark Royal*), their effect on the North African battle was slight, while they were sadly missed in the Atlantic. Another six were detached on Hitler's orders to Norway, to operate against Russian convoys. Their sinkings were few.

The Royal Navy had done well in 1941 and it is true that there was a gleam of light, but the overall picture was still dark. UK and Commonwealth shipyards had built one million tons of merchant shipping in 1941 but losses exceeded four and a quarter million tons, half due to U-boats. It was estimated that the UK needed thirty-six million tons of dry cargo per year, but imports fell nine million tons short of this. Worse, oil stocks, already low, fell by a further 318,000 tons. Sinkings of merchant ships were still only at 38 per cent of the 1917 figures and were certain to increase as the new U-boats became operational.[3] Between April and December 1941, thirty U-boats were sunk, an increasing number by corvettes, though destroyers were still the biggest scorers (see table 4.1).

Designed in response to criticisms of the Flower class, and initially referred to as 'twin-screw corvettes', the River class were a big improvement, but did not enter service until 1942. The River class differed little one from another, but *Nadder*, shown here, is unusual in mounting Oerlikons on the forecastle.

Table 4.1: Causes of U-boat sinkings, April–December 1941	
Surface vessels	21
Aircraft	4
Submarine	2
Mines	0
Accident and unknown	3

Type 271 radar. The original lantern had thick wooden framing which caused side echoes (a). A lighter version was introduced with more perspex (b). The lantern was usually covered in port (c) so that the dimensions of the aerial (d) could not be measured since this would disclose the operating frequency. (John Lambert)

Technical and Other Developments

The year 1941 saw the introduction of a considerable number of developments, both of equipment and of its operational use. Their full effect would not be seen until a later phase of the battle and was delayed by the U-boat assault on US coastal shipping.

Centimetric Radar[4]

Better things were on the way; a new lightweight, rotating aerial based on that used in the 281 was tried in *Legion* in February 1941. It could detect a merchant ship at nine miles, a destroyer at five

and a surfaced submarine at one and a half miles. By September 1941, thirty-seven ships (thirty convoy escorts) had this new aerial 286P, compared with 210 ships with earlier, fixed aerials.

Early in 1940, there were three developments, including the cavity magnetron, which made possible the use of much shorter wavelengths in the 10cm range. By November, a working set was tried in Swanage Bay. It detected the submarine *Usk*, stern-on, at seven and a half miles, and with the conning tower only showing at four to four and a half miles.

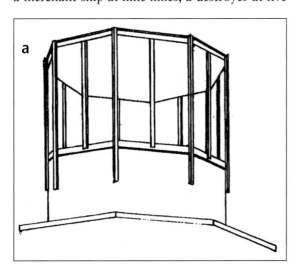

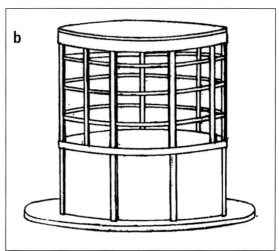

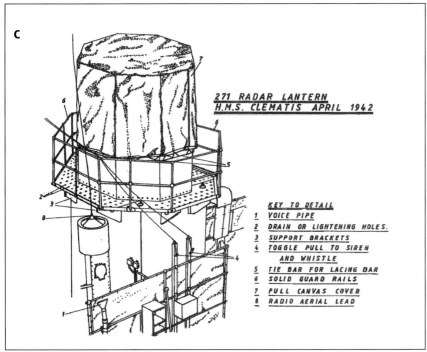

271 RADAR LANTERN
H.M.S. CLEMATIS APRIL 1942

KEY TO DETAIL
1 VOICE PIPE
2 DRAIN OR LIGHTENING HOLES.
3 SUPPORT BRACKETS
4 TOGGLE PULL TO SIREN
   AND WHISTLE
5 TIE BAR FOR LACING BAR
6 SOLID GUARD RAILS
7 FULL CANVAS COVER
8 RADIO AERIAL LEAD

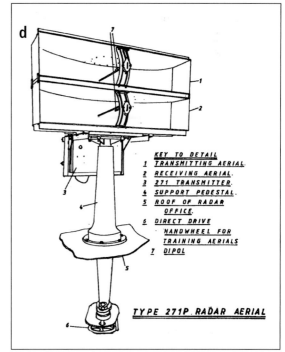

KEY TO DETAIL
1 TRANSMITTING AERIAL.
2 RECEIVING AERIAL.
3 271 TRANSMITTER.
4 SUPPORT PEDESTAL.
5 ROOF OF RADAR
   OFFICE.
6 DIRECT DRIVE
   HANDWHEEL FOR
   TRAINING AERIALS
7 DIPOL

TYPE 271P RADAR AERIAL

A very simple set was devised and the first twelve units were built at Eastney. In February 1941 the brave decision was made to order 150 Type 271 sets in advance of trials and increase the Eastney build to twenty-four. Though waveguides[5] were known, there was no experience with them, and the aerial feed was a coaxial cable. This had to be short, so that the aerial was on the roof of the radar office. This unit was quite big and heavy and there were difficulties in fitting in some classes. However, the Flowers had sufficient space and stability for the new set. The aerial was contained within a lantern with teak pillars framing flat, perspex panels, sand-blasted so that the aerial itself could not be seen (which would allow its operating frequency to be deduced).

The first Eastney set was fitted in *Orchis* during March 1941, while she was under repair at Scotts (Greenock). Trials began on 25 March in calm weather, with destroyers and the Norwegian submarine B1. As usual on trials, there is always calm when rough weather is wanted. However, rough-weather trials began on 1 April, with *Orchis* rolling and yawing violently. The detection range against the small submarine was 2.1 miles in rough seas, 2.5 in calm; destroyers were picked up at about 6 miles, buoys at 1 mile and high land 'off scale' at over 14 miles.

The twenty-four sets from Eastney and another 100 from the Allen West company were designated Mk II and a further 1,000 from Metropolitan Vickers, re-engineered for production, became the Mk III. These late sets had almost identical performance to the *Orchis* prototype but required much less maintenance. By May 1942, a year after the *Orchis* trials, there were 236 RN ships at sea with 271 or its derivatives. Most ships with 286 had been converted to 286PQ with a rotating aerial and improved performance. A redesigned 1.5-metre set, 291, was tried in *Ambuscade* in February 1942. Also early in 1942 an ingenious scheme was put in force to aid ship-fitting of 271. All components and the huts were sent to a factory,[6] where the ship's radar office was completely fitted out. Installation on board took place in two successive boiler cleans, each lasting about a

week. During the first, the steel supporting structure was built, and three months later the hut with superimposed aerial was dropped on and connected.

There were remarkably few problems. Early installations suffered from much larger side lobes than expected, a problem traced to the teak framing of the lantern. The solution was a six-foot moulded cylinder of perspex, tried in *Hesperus* in December 1942. In August 1942, a PPI display was tried in *Watchman*, and fitting followed by mid-1943. Type 272 had a waveguide feeding the aerial, so that the office could be a short distance from the aerial. This made ship-fitting less of a problem and many destroyers and sloops had the lantern on a short lattice mast aft. Type 273 had a different aerial and was used in big ships.

In August 1941, a team at Birmingham University developed the 'strapped magnetron', which enabled the transmitting power of the 271 to increase from 5kW to 70kW. On the first test, this extra power merely burnt out the cable, but once the cable was replaced with a waveguide, which doubled the aerial gain, all was well. The 271Q was designed to use the same office, panels and cabinets as the original set, so the update was simple. The first trial was on the *Marigold* in May 1942 (at the same time as Hedgehog trials), when it was found that a trimmed-down submarine could be detected at five miles, roughly double that of the early 271s. Production began in December 1942 (272 was not updated but replaced). Later and better types were to follow – but the battle was won by the 271.

High Frequency Direction Finding (HF/DF) – commonly 'Huff Duff'

The German control system for wolf packs depended on two-way ship–shore communication using HF radio. They were well aware that such transmissions could be located using direction finding but thought that the apparatus needed was so large that it could not be fitted in a ship. The cross-bearing, or 'cut', obtained in mid-Atlantic between two shore-based sets would be too inexact for operational use. As a result, the Germans concluded that over 200 kilometres from shore was safe. HF signals travel in a straight line and hence direct transmissions can only be received by ships in line of sight, ie within the horizon, known as the 'ground signal'. However, signals are also reflected in the ionosphere – the 'sky wave' – and this signal can be received at any distance.

The experienced operator could learn a lot from the signal itself. It was usually possible to distinguish between the ground wave and the sky wave – the former indicating that the source was within about fifteen to twenty miles. The strict German procedures made it possible to recognise some standard groups, even when the full message could not be read. Such groups might indicate a sighting report or the start of an attack. There would normally be a very short, high-priority sighting signal followed by an amplifying message. The HF/DF operator might well be able to recognise the signs of a wet aerial from a U-boat that had just surfaced. Sometimes it was even possible to identify individual U-boats from the characteristic key style of their operator.[7]

The Allies were fully aware of the value of ship-borne HF/DF and went to great lengths to guard its secrecy. Intercepted messages formed an important input into the Ultra code-breaking effort and the system was given the same security level until well after the war. Unaware of HF/DF, the Germans ascribed unexplained contacts to the use of radar, so that even when their documents were examined after the war there was no indication that they appreciated the value of DF.[8] In consequence there has been very little published on the way in which British and Polish scientists developed ship-borne HF/DF and the RN and other navies used it operationally. Indeed, Rohwer credits HF/DF as being the major factor in the great convoy battles of 1943.

In the autumn of 1940 an electronic surveillance vessel was fitted out. The ship chosen was the *Beachy*, already fitting out as a rescue ship. She was intended to listen for radar transmissions from U-boats and also for radio communications.[9] Her first voyage was with convoy OB226 on 10 October 1940 and she appears to have confirmed the use of HF radio for communications. *Beachy* reverted to the rescue-ship role – the first in service – and was sunk by air attack on 11 January 1941. Work was already in hand on HF/DF and a prototype, FH1, went to sea in *Hesperus* in March 1940. It appears to have been unsuccessful as no more were produced and an FH2 went to sea in August 1941. This and other early sets could not distinguish between the true bearing and its reciprocal.

The biggest problem was in the aerial. It was soon apparent that it should be at the highest point of the ship, the foremast head. By the time that HF/DF went to sea, this site had been claimed by radar (286) and HF/DF had to accept a shorter mast aft. Accuracy was good within the ground-wave reception (fifteen to twenty miles).

HF/DF aerial, used for both the FH3 and FH4 sets with insignificant differences.

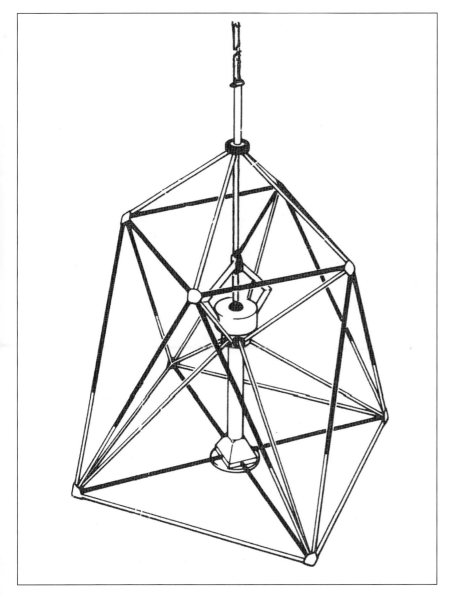

Later in the war, radar 271 moved down and HF/DF took the top site. Later still, Type 293 became the standard surface-warning radar and this was normally carried at the top of a lattice mast, with a pole topmast for the HF/DF. The height of the aerial left it exposed to icing and wind, which meant that its elements had to be strong but not too heavy, as escorts were already having stability problems due to extra topweight. Aerial design came under a Polish engineer, Struszynski, working at the ASE (Signal School) under the overall leadership of C Crampton. The earliest sets, the FH3, went to sea late in 1941, the prototypes in the fleet destroyers *Gurkha* and *Lance* in July 1941. Ship-fitting built up rapidly in 1942 (twenty-five escorts fitted by January 1942), reaching the planned total by the middle of the year. The FH3 set was superseded by the FH4 in 1943 but there was no obvious change in the aerial. The FH4 set had been developed by Plessey with ASE and featured a visual (cathode ray tube) presentation rather than the aural presentation of the FH3. The prototype FH4 went to sea in the ex-USCG *Culver* in October 1941 and was first in action in *Leamington* in March 1942, on convoy WS17. The French, too, had made progress; their team moved to the USA at the fall of France and formed the basis for the USN work.

When there was only a single HF/DF set with a convoy, there was a slight risk of plotting a reciprocal bearing, though the tactical plot would usually make it clear which bearing was relevant and the developed aerial made a reciprocal almost impossible.[10] A single set gave no range, though the operator would usually recognise the ground wave as 'close' (fifteen to twenty miles). Two sets, or better three, would give a cross-bearing and hence an accurate position for the transmitter. Since there were numerous frequencies available for the U-boats, a greater number of ship sets increased the chance of an intercept. If this shadowing U-boat could be sunk or even kept down, there was an opportunity for a change of course to evade other boats.

HF/DF was particularly valuable in locating the tracker U-boat, which could be sunk or, at least, forced to dive, disrupting the wolf pack

concentration. Priority in fitting seems to have been given to ships carrying the senior officer of the escort. Since his ship would usually be in the van of the convoy, it was logical to give second priority to the rescue ship, normally at the rear, to give as long a base for bearings as possible.

Howse describe a typical action due to HF/DF on 23 August 1942 with convoy ON 122. First contact was made on HF/DF by *Viscount* and the rescue ship *Stockport*. They directed the corvette *Potentilla* (Norwegian manned) to the transmitter and she made radar contact forty-five minutes later at two and a half miles. The submarine dived but was picked up by propeller noise at three-quarters of a mile and then by active asdic. Three depth charge attacks were carried out and U-256 was severely damaged. On the way home, she was bombed in the Bay of Biscay on 31 August and out of action for a year.[11]

By mid-1943, the Germans had abundant evidence of the use of ship-borne HF/DF, but they were obsessed by radar and the evidence was ignored. Decoded radio messages referred to HF/DF, and agents in Spain regularly photographed RN ships off Gibraltar showing the aerial. It was even painted out when some photos were reproduced for recognition books.[12] Many U-boat COs were suspicious and noted that attacks followed quickly after a radio transmission. Very late in the war, the Germans developed the Kurier burst transmitter, which was almost impossible to DF.

Communications

Escort vessels needed rapid, secure communications with other escorts for tactical control, merchant ships (particularly for diversions) and with HQ on shore. The means available in 1939 included flags, which could be used only in daylight. Flashing lights could be used at any time but there were few merchantmen who could read reliably. Medium-frequency radio using Morse code was available but it could be intercepted and located at a considerable distance and hence was rarely used. Loud hailer and the older megaphone were used but messages were too liable to descend into mutual abuse. Flags and flashing lights were suitable

The River class *Plym*'s large quarterdeck is full of depth charge gear. Note the HF/DF aerial at the masthead. She came to an unusual end, being expended in an atomic bomb trial.

only for short messages, for example a code word for a prearranged procedure such as a diversionary course change. This limitation emphasised the need for common training.

Ship-to-ship voice radio was introduced in 1941 using medium frequency but, like its Morse predecessor, it was easily intercepted and hence little used. The US VHF TBS was introduced to the RN in 1943 and proved very valuable and reliable. TBS greatly improved the escort commander's control of his group.

Code Breaking

All German services relied on signal encoding via the multi-rotor Enigma machine, which they believed was unbreakable. Of their potential opponents, Poland came closest to breaking Enigma and early in 1939 they handed over their work to France and the UK. The German naval Enigma had one more rotor than those of the other services and proved very hard to break. During 1940 and early 1941 the British acquired a number of rotors, often as a result of captures of weather ships intended to obtain cipher material. As described earlier in this chapter, the big breakthrough came on 9 May

1941, when U-110 was boarded by a party from HMS *Bulldog*, which captured a complete machine with code settings and other material. Another weather ship was boarded on 28 June, giving settings for July.

For the rest of 1941, most naval signals could be read fairly quickly, enabling the Admiralty to divert convoys away from U-boat concentrations. U-boat Command had some suspicions of a leak of cipher materials and tried various tricks to make their messages more secure. However, they still believed that Enigma itself was unbreakable. The value to the convoy system was very great; Rohwer estimates a saving of 1.5–2 million tons in the second half of 1941. President Roosevelt had involved the USN to an increasing extent in the western Atlantic and decoded messages were used to reduce the number of clashes between US ships and U-boats.

It is difficult to compare the successes of Bletchley Park and B-Dienst, since there were periods in which one or the other had a partial ability to read enemy messages, but possibly taking too long for tactical use. In summary, the Germans could read British signals from

September 1939 to August 1940, and from February 1943 to June 1943; the British could read German signals from June 1941 to February 1942 (the introduction of the four-rotor Enigma machine), and from December 1942 to the end of the war.

Training

The RCN had a work-up base at Pictou, Nova Scotia in 1941 and at Digby, also in Nova Scotia, in 1943. Both were susceptible to bad weather, even though training was transferred to Halifax in winter months. Eventually, in 1944, a satisfactory solution was found with HMS *Somers Isle* in Bermuda.

The need for group training was appreciated but there were a number of difficulties, notably that the shortage of escorts made it difficult to keep the ships of a group together. Before taking up his appointment as commander-in-chief, Sir Percy Noble went as a 'passenger' on the leader of one group, but before the voyage was complete every other ship in the group had been diverted on Admiralty orders.

Aces

Among both submarine captains and their hunters, a disproportionate number of sinkings were due to a small number of aces. Men such as Walker and Gretton and, on the other side, Kretschmer and Prien, and a very few others on both sides, distort all statistics. Much of their success was due to natural skills enhanced by dedication and hard work. However, once their reputation was established, men such as Walker got the best ships and the best captains and were selected to operate in areas where the action was keen.

There was one big difference between the fate of the British hunters and their German opponents. Some RN aces admitted to burn-out and were rested in shore jobs where they could pass on much of their expertise to a new generation. Walker died of a heart attack. Even when still serving at sea, they were encouraged to visit training centres, where they could pass on their ideas to others and even learn new ideas themselves.

U-boat aces usually went on till they were

sunk. It is well said that 'There are old U-boat captains and bold U-boat captains but there are few old, bold U-boat captains.' Table 4.2 shows the top-scoring U-boat commanders in the spring of 1941.

Table 4.2: Top-scoring U-boat captains (spring 1941)		
Commander	Tonnage sunk	U-boat
Günther Prien	245,000	U-47
Joachim Schepke	230,000	U-100
Otto Kretschmer	282,000	U-99

Within little more than a week, all three had gone. During the night of 7–8 March, U-47, with four other submarines (including U-99), was operating against convoy OB293. Prien attacked on the surface, just before dusk, under cover of a rain squall. Visibility suddenly cleared, showing U-47 in clear view of the destroyer *Wolverine*. Prien made a sharp turn and attempted to escape on the surface. The destroyer was slowed by heavy seas and Prien should have got away but, foolishly, he dived. *Wolverine* steamed in and released a pattern of depth charges set shallow. U-47 was fatally damaged; in particular, the propeller shafts were put out of alignment making them very noisy. Prien had not given up and surfaced to escape. The noisy shafts gave her away and *Wolverine* came in again. U-47 dived and another shallow pattern was followed by a massive underwater explosion. Wreckage came to the surface – one down.

Convoy HX112 was sighted on the evening of 15 March by U-110, which homed in four more U-boats, including U-99 and U-100, to the scene. The escort was the 5th Escort Group, led by Cdr Macintyre, with five elderly destroyers and two Flowers. U-100 sank a tanker that night, and the following night U-99 sank three tankers and two other steamers totalling 34,505 tons. U-100 then came in again and was picked up at 1,000 yards by *Vanoc*'s primitive 286 radar (the first such detection). Schepke tried to escape on the surface but the old destroyer was too fast for him and rammed U-100 amidships, crushing Schepke against the periscope standard. There were six survivors. Macintyre suggests that Schepke was deceived by *Vanoc*'s Western

Ness, a standard River.

Approaches camouflage scheme.

Shortly afterwards, *Walker* made asdic contact with a submerged submarine. The depth charge crews had not completed reloading after a previous abortive attack but six charges were dropped in a snap attack. Immediately, a submarine was sighted surfaced and stopped astern. Every gun that would bear opened fire, but with no fire control there were few hits and little damage was done. Eventually the U-boat signalled that she was 'sunking [*sic*]'. Forty men of the U-99, including Kretschmer, still wearing his cap, were picked up, to the delight of thirty-eight survivors of a merchant ship rescued by *Walker* a little earlier. Kretschmer had a special pair of Zeiss binoculars, presented by Dönitz, and these came to Macintyre as a prize of war.

Walker had made earlier contacts that did not lead to a kill, including one where the first contact was the visual sighting of a surfaced submarine wake.

The lessons were well known, even at that date, and it is surprising that three aces fell foul of them. Visual sighting was vital, though

Vanoc's radar contact gave a blurred view of the future. A submarine caught on the surface should stay there and run, heading into the sea. Even the faster destroyers had difficulty in catching a submarine at night and an unstabilised 4in gun without fire control was unlikely to hit, let alone cause fatal damage. Ramming was reliable, but costly in terms of the damage to the escort.

Twin-Screw Corvettes – River class Frigates

As soon as the Flower class corvettes entered service, there were complaints. Many of these were unjustified but it was clear that these corvettes, designed for coastal operation, were far from ideal for Atlantic work. A meeting was called on 27 November 1940 to consider the requirements for an A/S escort. Those attending included senior representatives of relevant staff divisions and A P Cole, RCNC, who was asked to make a rough estimate of the size and power of the desired vessel.[13] It was noted that it might be necessary to 'trim some of the requirements to bring them into the realm of practicability'. The 'wish list' included:

- good sea-keeping to keep company with a convoy in any weather;
- speed of at least 20 knots – 22 if possible – with good acceleration and astern power;
- endurance of 3,500–4,000 miles (UK–Freetown);
- small turning circle;
- simple machinery, easy to maintain;
- armament of one 4in HA/LA (two in bigger ship), two 2pdr, two Oerlikons, with simple fire control; if second 4in fitted, director with Type 285;
- four depth charge throwers each side and two traps (fourteen pattern) with 100 charges (it was noted that new methods of throwing depth charges were being tried, presumably ahead-throwing);
- asdics (unspecified), ASV (radar), W/T and R/T;
- SA gear (sweep for dealing with acoustic mines); wire minesweeping;
- stem stiffened for ramming but 'rounded' for asdic reasons;
- small crew.

DNC thought that this could be met by a ship of about 1,500 tons, 300–20 feet in length (soon revised to 350 feet). Diesel engines could not be relied on for continuous high speed. Steam reciprocating engines needed too much space and could not accelerate rapidly. Turbines of at least 12,000shp would be needed and would take about eighteen months to produce. The meeting then considered the conversion of the ex-US Town class to long-range escorts (qv). This 'wish list' conflicted with the need for the vessels to be cheap and easy to build using existing facilities – shipyards, engine works and armament manufacturers.

The design was directed by A W Watson (who had designed the P boats of World War 1; Goodall was to remark in his diary for 18 June 1940, 'Watson is a really good man'), with Kimberley as the constructor in direct charge. A first study suggested that the requirements implied a ship of about 350 feet in length, with turbine machinery and a lightweight hull to warship standards. Production constraints dictated that such a ship could not be built in numbers; available slips limited the length to about 300 feet and there was no capacity for turbine machinery. The A/S armament would be the same as a corvette – asdic and depth

The River class *Derg* in 1943 seems to have minesweeping gear as well as fourteen-pattern depth charge gear.

Helmsdale was one of the few Rivers with turbine machinery. She remained in service longer than most, being used for trials of ASW equipment.

charges – but far more of them. Design seems to have begun in about November 1940, when it was still referred to as a twin-screw corvette, and a design study approved by the end of the month. By December, Goodall was concerned that they were getting too complicated and Watson was told to simplify.

The hull structure was relatively light, though complying with Classification Societies Rules (Lloyd's Register and British Corporation); some warship experience was incorporated and it was easy to build. The Societies' surveyors supervised the building. The preparation of building drawings was divided among the shipbuilders. Some builders saved up to thirty tons by the use of welding.

The machinery consisted of two sets of Flower class triple-expansion engines, slightly modified with a drive off either end of the crankshaft to suit the right- and left-handed twin shaft arrangement. This gave a speed of just under twenty knots, at least faster than a surfaced U-boat. Six ships were powered by a twin shaft turbine plant of 6,500shp, giving twenty and a half knots.

Table 4.3: River class frigates (as designed)
Displacement (tons): 1,855 deep
Dimensions (feet): 301¼ oa x 36½ x 13 deep
Shp and speed (kts): 5,500 = 19.5
Fuel (tons), endurance miles @ (kts): 470, 5,000 @ 15 (clean bottom)
Complement: 114

The designed armament was two single 4in Mk XIX HA/LA guns (60° elevation, 1,300ft/sec muzzle velocity) and ten 20mm Oerlikons. Because of the shortage of guns, most carried only four Oerlikons. The single Oerlikons were later replaced by twin power mounts in most. Many had HF/DF at the masthead and 271 on the bridge. A few had the bridge set replaced by 277 later. Some had a 6pdr on the forecastle, either side of the Hedgehog.[14]

There were eight depth charge throwers (fourteen pattern) and 100 depth charges. Four throwers were later removed and the number of charges increased to 154, with asdic 144. There was a Hedgehog on the forecastle (Hedgehog had not been developed when the ship design was started). The first twenty ships were fitted for minesweeping but the gear was later removed, allowing them to carry an extra eighty-five tons of fuel. After the twenty ships of the first programme and four of the next programme, fuel capacity was increased to 650 tons, giving 7,500 miles endurance. All Canadian ships had the longer endurance.

The long forecastle gave good stability at large angles of heel, even when the inevitable weight growth took place. Similarly, the deep hull kept stresses low, reducing the risk of their breaking their back when torpedoed.

Rother was treated as 'first of class' (though beaten to sea by *Exe*) and carried out a full programme of trials in spring 1942.[15] At a displacement of 1,900 tons, she achieved 19¾ knots with 5,535ihp at 184rpm. Cost was quoted as

£240,000. Reports from sea were generally favourable, the long forecastle keeping much of the ship dry while the covered access fore and aft made life more pleasant. The low quarterdeck was wet, affecting the depth charge crews. The Hedgehog was exposed and wet. It seems that there was an intention to replace it with a split mounting either side of the forward gun, but only *Monnow* was so altered. The fact that few changes were made in service shows that the original concept was right.

A total of fifty-seven ships were built in the UK; Canada built ten for the RN (two were transferred to the USN) and thirty-nine for the RCN. Twenty-two more were built in Australia with slightly different armament, providing increased AA for the Pacific war. These took no part in the Atlantic battle and are not discussed.

The Rivers were very good ships when they appeared in 1942 but with so many later ships available they were soon paid off by the RN. Their only fault lay in their late arrival; what a pity that a prototype had not been built before the war. Some attractive and effective modernisations of Canadian ships, planned by Rowland Baker, showed what was possible.

Monnow was the only River to have a split Hedgehog on the forward gun deck. (IWM A22681)

HMCS *Jonquiere* shown post-war after a modernisation designed by (Sir) Rowland Baker, RCNC.

5 The Second Happy Time:
January–June 1942

The entry of the USA into the war following Pearl Harbor was seen by the U-boat staff as presenting both short-term advantages and long-term dangers. It was appreciated that it would take the USN some considerable time to introduce convoys for their east coast shipping, which would make fine targets for the increasing number of U-boats entering front-line service. On the other hand, they correctly estimated that the might of American industry would greatly increase the rate at which new merchant ships and escorts would be built and put into service.

In June 1942 the German estimate was that the Allied total merchant shipbuilding output for the year would be about seven million tons, a figure which proved to be almost exactly correct. To destroy the Allied shipping capability, it was estimated that U-boats must sink 800,000 tons each month (200,000 more than the corresponding figure in 1917). This figure was never going to be easy; in the last six months of 1941 the monthly rate was only about 125,000 tons, but in that period the number of boats on station was between fourteen and seventeen. In early 1942 it was expected that this number would increase rapidly. However, Hitler insisted on a strong force in the Mediterranean – about twenty in late 1941 – and another twenty to protect Norway. It is of interest that the Norway-based U-boats sank only twenty-five ships in the seven months to July, and of these, no less than sixteen came from the ill-fated PQ17 convoy.

The first wave was far fewer in numbers than Dönitz wanted: two Type IX and three Type X[1] boats deployed between Newfoundland and Cape Hatteras. At the same time, seven Type VIIC were sent to operate to the south of Newfoundland. The appalling cold weather and heavy groundswell over the Grand Banks caused many torpedo failures and they sank only two or three ships each. Two more Type VIIC followed in February and these ventured further south to Cape Hatteras. In doing so they demonstrated that the endurance of this class could be stretched by about three weeks as a result of the acceptance by the crew of great hardship. The deck of the passageway was covered with layers of tinned food and at least one toilet cubicle was packed with food.

There was no convoy system off the US coast until the middle of May; shipping followed pre-war routes close to the shore. There was no blackout in coastal towns, so that, at night, ships were silhouetted against this bright background. Lighthouses, buoys and even ships' own navigation lights were left burning as in peacetime. The few escorts, mainly World War I PC and 'Eagle' boats were deployed as 'hunting groups'. There were also a few, very effective, Coast Guard cutters. The old fallacy was dragged out – that a weakly defended convoy was worse than no convoy – and once again proved wrong. Starting on 1 April, a limited escort system was operated. Ships would be escorted during daylight hours by auxiliary patrol vessels, armed yachts and the like, and spend the night in defended anchorages.

The RN lent ten corvettes and twenty-two A/S trawlers from their own escort force. An American building programme began to deliver

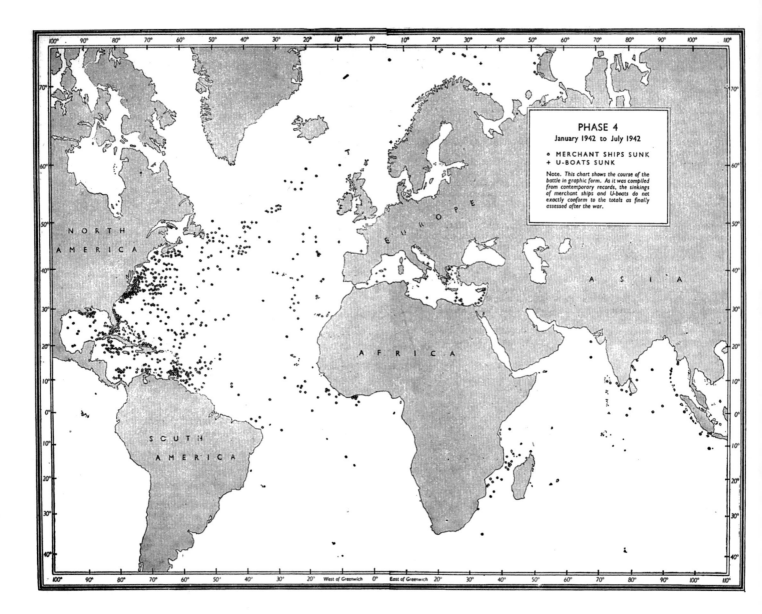

PHASE 4
January 1942 to July 1942

• MERCHANT SHIPS SUNK
+ U-BOATS SUNK

Note. *This chart shows the course of the battle in graphic form. As it was compiled from contemporary records, the sinkings of merchant ships and U-boats do not exactly conform to the totals as finally assessed after the war.*

Phase 4 of the Atlantic battle: the U-boats' second 'Happy Time'. Sinkings were almost all in the Eastern Atlantic, mostly but not entirely very close to the coasts of the USA and Caribbean islands.

both A/S vessels and also minesweepers that could be used in the A/S role. The USN had relearned the lessons of 1917–18, though at tragic cost. By mid-May a full convoy system was in operation and losses off the USA fell rapidly. Dönitz switched his attack to the Caribbean, made possible by the entry into service of the first two U-tankers, Type XIV milch cows (see the next section). They could carry enough fuel to extend the endurance of the Type VIIs by about four weeks. The four-rotor Enigma machines came into use in February 1942, and for the rest of that year the U-boat code could not be read at Bletchley Park. This silence added greatly to the safety of the Type XIV boats, which had to use

radio to communicate with their customers. From mid-May until convoy was introduced in the Caribbean in mid-July, losses were again heavy but fell off with the use of convoys.

The number of U-boats at sea rose from forty-two in January to seventy in July, but that includes boats in transit as well as those in the Mediterranean and off Norway. There were rarely more than a dozen in the rich grounds off America. In January 1942 there were 110 RN and 67 RCN Flowers in the Atlantic, plus a few sloops and destroyers. The great majority of sinkings by surface ships was still attributed to destroyers (see table 5.1).

Painful as these losses in early 1942 had

been, they were not decisive; worldwide, the monthly sinkings had averaged about 480,000 tons (with a worst month – June – of 637,000), far less than the target of 800,000 tons. The U-boat staff estimate of merchant shipbuilding also fell short of the reality in 1943. They estimated a total build of 10.8 million tons, whereas the actual output was 15.1 million tons. But the darkest hour is just before the dawn.

Table 5.1: Causes of U-boat sinkings, January–June 1942	
Surface vessels	17½
Aircraft	10½
Submarine	1
Mines	1
Accident and unknown	2

Technical Developments

Much development work was going on but, in most cases, the resulting equipments were only available in a later period.

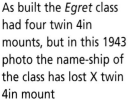

As built the *Egret* class had four twin 4in mounts, but in this 1943 photo the name-ship of the class has lost X twin 4in mount

Asdic

The Type 144 owed much to the earlier 128 but was completely redesigned. Type 144 used the retractable dome of Type 128, and the very similar 145 for slower ships used the detachable dome of the 'trawler' set Type 123. It is sometimes suggested that the 123/145 sets were inferior in capability, but this is not so; the slower ships did not need a retractable dome.

The design of the 144 began in about May 1941 and the first sets entered service a little over a year later. It was designed to control ahead-throwing weapons, first Hedgehog and then Squid, but could also direct a conventional depth charge attack. The electronics were redesigned to improve discrimination, picking out a target from background noise. Range and bearing recorders were also redesigned and drove repeaters on the bridge and in the wheelhouse. These provided data on the course to be steered and the point at which the weapon was to be fired. The slope of the trace gave closing speed. The transducer trained automatically in 5° steps (half that as it trained across the ends of a target), so that the operator only had to select port or starboard.

Codes

On 1 February 1942 the Germans introduced an additional rotor to their Enigma machines, multiplying the number of solutions twenty-six times. Enigma was unreadable for many months, though direction finding was becoming more useful with HF/DF sets on many ships. The pattern of signals also helped. On 30 October

1942, U-559 was blown to the surface by the destroyer *Petard* and the weather code book was recovered, though two sailors were drowned trying to get the Enigma machine. The code book was printed with water-soluble ink but much was readable. With this as a crib, the machine cipher was solved – with difficulty, but by December Bletchley Park was reading most signals (with some delay).

The blackout in decoding Enigma coincided with the second 'Happy Time' for the U-boats, in early 1942 off the eastern coast of the USA. But it was not a direct cause, as the number of ships sunk fell dramatically when US coastal convoys were introduced. By early February 1943, signals were being read with little delay. On the other side of the hill, B-Dienst had broken Allied Cipher No. 3 and was decrypting some 80 per cent of signals, though there was considerable delay and probably only about 10 per cent were read in time to be of use.

Type XIV U-boats – Milch Cows

During the winter of 1939/40, U-boat Command considered means of increasing the time on station, in particular, reducing the time spent in transit. This led to idea of a 'U-tanker', carrying a large quantity of fuel, which could be transferred at sea to the attack boats. The Type XIV was the result; based on the Type IX but shorter, it carried 432 tons of fuel supply (figures differ), as well as 203 tons for its own use. Own fuel and cargo were interchangeable. The Type XIV had no armament other than light AA, giving more internal space. This meant that it could carry a considerable quantity of provisions (thirty tons), with a large cold room. It also carried spare parts and fifteen tons of lubricating oil, and could supply fresh water. There was a doctor, who could visit customer U-boats and carry out minor treatments. More-seriously ill or injured men could be brought on to the XIV and exchanged for one of her crew.

They completed in small numbers from the end of 1941, but it was well into 1942 before the first was operational. Before long, it became clear that the greatest benefit was not so much in reducing transit time but more in reducing the frequency of crossing the hazardous waters of the Bay of Biscay.

The refuelling operation was difficult and lengthy. First, the customer had to make contact with its tanker. This was usually done by specifying a square on the U-boat grid. However, each square was six miles across and submariners were reluctant to use lights and even more so to use radio homing. Once contact was made, a line had to be got across, usually using a rubber dinghy with the submarines stopped some 80–100 metres apart. The line would then be used to pull the hose across and fuelling could begin. The pumping rate was 30–35 tons per hour but not much more than half that rate was achieved, allowing for interruptions. While this was going, on the doctor could visit, lubrication oil would be supplied through a different hose and provisions would be transferred. The demand for provisions was usually slight, although fresh bread was welcome. Often, a second customer would be waiting. The exercise was dangerous and there was a steady toll of men lost overboard.

Arranging a meeting involved several signals between the boats and HQ. The introduction of the Type XIV coincided with a blackout on Enigma, making their frequent use of radio less dangerous. From early 1943, these signals were being read by Bletchley Park; most milch cows were sunk in mid-1943, only U-490 surviving into 1944.

Post-war analysis suggests that the concept of replenishment U-tankers was valid and cost-effective. However, this was true only if arrangements for a meeting could be made without the signals being either read or used for direction finding.

Later Sloops – *Black Swan*

The concept of the general-purpose sloop was gradually abandoned. In 1931 the minesweeping function was devolved to the *Halcyon* class of specialist sweepers. *Fleetwood* showed the potential of a heavy, mainly AA, armament (two twin 4in guns) and in 1933 this led to the 'ocean convoy sloop'. The first of these was *Bittern*; however, she completed as the Admiralty Yacht *Enchantress*, and her sister *Stork* became a

Black Swan with pom-pom on the quarterdeck.

survey vessel. The third, finally taking the name *Bittern*, completed with the intended armament of three twin 4in AA guns. This was a very heavy armament when the latest cruisers had only four twin 4in AA. The mountings were unstabilised and to improve their accuracy it was decided to fit *Bittern* with the, then, novel Denny-Brown active fin roll stabilisers (discussed later). Four similar ships were built for the RIN.

Sloop design was now in the hands of some outstanding constructors, led by Victor Shepheard (later Sir, DNC), with Ivor King (Director of Dockyards), followed by Rowland Baker (Sir, Dreadnought Project Team) as assistants. With *Grimsby*, the weight and stability problems of the early classes were finally overcome and the weighed weights of *Enchantress* were 'fantastically accurate (for which I take all credit.)'.[2]

Fin stabilisers were a personal enthusiasm of the new DNC, Stanley Goodall, who was to tell the RAN that they were wasting their money if they built an unstabilised sloop.[3] Control theory was in its infancy and it was easy for the fins to make things worse; there are delightful stories of *Bittern* rolling heavily in a calm sea. When they were set up by experts for a trial, the results were favourable but in less skilled hands they helped

little and many thought that the space they occupied would be more use as fuel tanks.

Bittern was followed by three ships of the *Egret* class with four twin 4in AA, although with only one HA director control tower (DCT) they could only engage a single target.[4] The first two ships of the *Black Swan* class were ordered under the 1937 programme and two more under the 1939 programme (with four for India). Initially, these two ships were fitted for wire minesweeping (*Black Swan* was fitted for minelaying). Another four were ordered under the 1940 programme, including *Whimbrel*, the last of these classes to survive, as the Egyptian *Tariq*. They were a little bigger than the *Egrets*, differing mainly in that the quarterdeck twin 4in gun was replaced by a four-barrel pom-pom. Some *Black Swan*s were fitted with Hedgehog by October 1945.[5]

Later ships had the beam increased to 38ft 6in and other changes, becoming the Modified *Black Swan* class. Further ships were ordered: fourteen under the 1940 Supplementary Estimates, eleven under 1941 (two cancelled) and three in 1944 (39ft 6in beam – all cancelled). The original design had a close-range AA armament of a four-barrel pom-pom on the quarterdeck and quadruple 0.5in machine guns

sited abaft the funnel. These were replaced by single Oerlikons, fitted on build in later ships. Single Oerlikons were fitted in the bridge wings in all ships as they became available, and replaced at the end of the war by single Bofors.

When the first ships of the 'Modified' class completed, light AA guns were still scarce and they received what was available. At least three ships had four-barrel pom-poms sited amidships, while others had twin power-operated

Left: An early shot of *Cygnet* with two 4 barrel pom-poms amidships.

Oerlikons. Eventually, most had two twin Bofors amidships, two twin Oerlikons on the quarterdeck and single Oerlikons on the bridge wings.

Table 5.2: *Black Swan* class
Displacement (tons): 1,960 deep
Dimensions (feet): 283 oa x 37¾ x 11¼
Shp and speed (kts): 4,300 = 19.25
Fuel (tons), endurance miles @ (kts): 420, 6,100 @ 15 (trial)
Complement: 192 (original)

Early ships completed with a tripod mast, which soon carried a Type 268 radar. Later a 271 was added on a short lattice mast aft and by the end of the war most had a lattice foremast with Type 293. The gun director had Type 285. Early ships had a considerable amount of splinter protection but most of this was later removed to restore stability.

There were eight depth charge throwers with up to 110 charges. Some had a split Hedgehog on B gun deck.[6] Asdic Type 144/147 was fitted. The effect of this increased armament can be seen in the electricity-generating capacity. Originally they had two 70kW steam-driven generators and one 50kW diesel-driven generator. This was increased to two 100kW steam and one 70kW diesel.

Their structure was to warship standards, although they were built of mild steel. Earlier ships were all riveted but the amount of welding gradually increased, with up to 30 per cent welded in some later ships. The design stresses in the original *Black Swan* were low: hogging/sagging figures were 5.7/5.0 tons/in^2 on deck and 3.7/4.3 tons/in^2 in the keel. Additional weights would have increased these stresses slightly but the deep hull to the long forecastle would have kept them on the low side. There are reports of splits in the forecastle deck, probably due to single-riveted seams. Cracks are also reported in the shell forward and in the area of the break of forecastle, well aft. There is no information on the cause but poor detail in these early examples of welding is probable. They were the Rolls-Royces of the escort force and their turbine machinery meant that they were built by experienced warship builders.

Wood decks were not fitted because of the shortage of timber, and other shortages led to a variety of unsatisfactory substitutes. The wood deck had also acted as thermal insulation to

Peacock is little changed in this 1951 photo by the author.

Left: Crane was a *Black Swan* class sloop, seen here in original configuration. Note the crowded quarterdeck.

spaces below, so that as the increased complement made condensation even worse, lagging was fitted and ventilation improved.

Capt F J Walker and the 2nd Escort Group[7]

The *Black Swan* class should always be associated with the memory of the 'ace' U-boat killer Capt 'Johnnie' Walker. Walker's naval career began as a cadet in the cruiser *Cornwall* in 1913 and he was a midshipman in *Ajax* when the First World War broke out. After promotion to sub-lieutenant in 1916 he spent the rest of the war in destroyers. As lieutenant, he served in *Sarpedon* and after the war in *Valiant*. In 1921 he began a series of courses that would make him one of the earliest ASW specialists in the RN. He was fleet A/S officer of the Atlantic Fleet in 1926–8, followed by a similar post in the Mediterranean until 1931, when he was made commander. He commanded the *Shikari* (control ship for the radio-controlled target *Centurion*) and then the *Falmouth*. From 1936–7 he was the commander of *Valiant*, after which he returned to A/S work as Experimental Commander at Portland. This could have been the end of his career, as he passed out of the zone for promotion to captain. When the war began, he was still at Portland but in January 1940 he joined the staff of Adm Ramsay at Dover, where he later played a part in planning the evacuation from Dunkirk.

In October 1941, Cdr Walker was appointed to command the 36th Escort Group from the sloop *Stork*. The rest of the group consisted of the older sloop *Deptford* and the corvettes *Vetch*, *Rhododendron*, *Pentstemon*, *Gardenia*, *Convolvulus*, *Samphire* and *Marigold*, though other vessels would reinforce the group from time to time. His group was mainly employed on the UK–Gibraltar run, where it was very much exposed to attack from both aircraft and U-boats based in France. By late 1941, the need to keep ships together as a group was appreciated, as was the need for training both as units and as a group. Walker would insist on training in harbour in such routine, but vital, tasks as the loading of depth charge throwers, introducing competition between ships. He introduced a standard tactical counter to a night surface attack (Buttercup). This was not perfect but was refined on the tactical table at Liverpool as the basis for many tactical ploys. This training began to show its benefits in the prolonged battle for convoy HG76, etc.

In April 1943, Walker transferred to command the 2nd Escort Group. He was now a captain, specially promoted to note his outstanding work, even though he was two years outside the normal zone for promotion. The 2nd Escort Group was to function as a support group to be used to reinforce the escort of a convoy under attack or to act against a concentration of U-boats located by other means. Quite specifically, the group's task was to sink U-boats and not primarily to ensure the safe passage of the convoy. They could sustain a prolonged hunt once a submarine was detected. This role is not to be confused with the early idea of hunting groups dashing madly about in the hope of finding a U-

Starling was Captain Walker's ship. She was directly concerned with sinking seven U-boats and present at the demise of several more.

boat. The support group concept was feasible because there were sufficient vessels to equip such groups as well as the basic convoy escort. Also, it was possible to identify U-boat concentrations by air search, HF/DF and Enigma.

Combined air–sea operations were valuable for a short period. U-boats had been given a heavy AA armament and a group of three boats could put up a lethal barrage, causing Coastal Command casualties in the Bay of Biscay to mount. A group of U-boats on the surface was fairly secure from air attack but if they dived, the aircraft could launch an attack on the point of submergence with a good chance of success. The U-boats' aim was to hold off the aircraft until they were short of fuel and had to return to base. However, if the aircraft could call on a support group, the situation changed. There was no way that the submarines could fight a surface gun duel with the powerfully armed sloops. If they dived, either the aircraft would score an immediate success or the group would launch a sustained asdic hunt.

Walker was an arch-tactician and managed to turn the most serious drawback of asdic to the advantage of the hunter. By the end of 1943 he had developed his 'creeping attack', which he usually called 'Operation Plaster'. One ship, usually Walker's own *Starling*, would maintain asdic contact with the submarine at ranges from 1,000 to 1,500 yards. The U-boat would be reassured by the steady ping that no attack was imminent and continue in an effort to escape at low, quiet speed – perhaps only two knots. One or more of the other ships of the group would then move slowly and quietly ahead of the locating ship. The position of the attackers would be established and when they were slightly ahead of the U-boat, to allow for the time needed for charges to reach the submarine's depth, a very large number (twenty-six) of depth charges would be released, set to the right depth. It is claimed that no U-boat evaded such an attack and hence Dönitz never learnt of it. It was also so successful that there is no record of 2nd Escort Group's using Hedgehog, though when *Loch Killin* joined there was no reluctance to use Squid. In an operation in January 1944, the group disposed of six U-boats, using 634 depth charges (*Woodpecker* was lost).

It was 'Johnnie' Walker's last operation. On 9 July 1944, he died after a stroke, probably brought on by stress. He was buried at sea from the famous Western Approaches destroyer *Hesperus*, as his own group was at work under Cdr Wemyss. His achievements are commemorated by a statue at Liverpool Pierhead. As Adm Horton said at the funeral service in Liverpool Cathedral:

Not dust nor the light weight of a stone, but all the sea of the Western Approaches shall be his tomb.

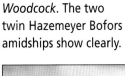

Woodcock. The two twin Hazemeyer Bofors amidships show clearly.

6 The Pendulum Swings:
August 1942–May 1943[1]

During the latter part of 1941, the principal problem facing the U-boat Command was that of locating convoys. The Atlantic covers a vast area and even a big convoy occupies a very small part of it. The range of vision from a U-boat, even in good conditions – and Atlantic weather was not often good – was small, and cooperation with Luftwaffe aircraft had not been very profitable.

By the time that the offensive off the American coasts petered out in mid-summer 1942, things had changed much in favour of the U-boats. The British Naval Cipher No. 3 had been broken by B-Dienst in February 1942 and most Allied signals in the Atlantic could be deciphered until June 1943. Signals on convoy routing and diversions could be read and even signals outlining Allied beliefs on U-boat disposition. The cipher war was swinging very much in Germany's favour as Bletchley Park was unable to read the four-rotor Enigma carrying the Triton code (code-named 'Shark' by the Allies). This was a very serious setback, but submarines on trial or training used a simpler code so that GCCS could follow a new U-boat until its first operation. After its departure, it could still be tracked by HF/DF, so that its position was known and its intention could be deduced from its movements.

The greatly increased number of U-boats at sea meant that the patrol lines could be extended and the chance of a convoy's escaping detection even with diversions was small. On the other hand, the increasing number of HF/DF sets at sea gave a high probability that the contact report would be picked up and the position of the sender determined. A surface escort or aircraft would be sent to the position so that the would-be shadower was, if not sunk, at least forced to dive. Once it had dived, its speed would be much reduced; even if only submerged for half an hour it would have lost a distance of perhaps four miles, which would take a considerable time on the surface to recover. In bad weather, the surface speed of a U-boat was only about three or four knots faster than the convoy, itself slowed.

On both sides, the effects of new technology and of training and operational experience were beginning to show. The British introduced the Type 271M 10cm radar from September 1941, which gave an all-round picture of the convoy and surfaced U-boats. It could even pick up a periscope in calm seas. HF/DF sets were comparatively numerous. Once contact was made, the new A/S mortar, Hedgehog, was in general service, *Westcott* claiming its first victim on 2 February 1942. There were many more escorts and it was usually possible to have both an outer and an inner screen, so that U-boats attempting to shadow could be forced down before getting close. Coastal Command was increasing its patrols in the Bay of Biscay and scoring successes with ASV II radar and the Leigh Light. U-boat Command countered with a radar detector, Metox, which was effective until February 1943, when the RAF introduced ASV III centimetric radar.

The RN was also benefiting from improved training, both of individual ships at Tobermory and of groups by Gilbert Roberts. The latter training emphasised the need to keep a group

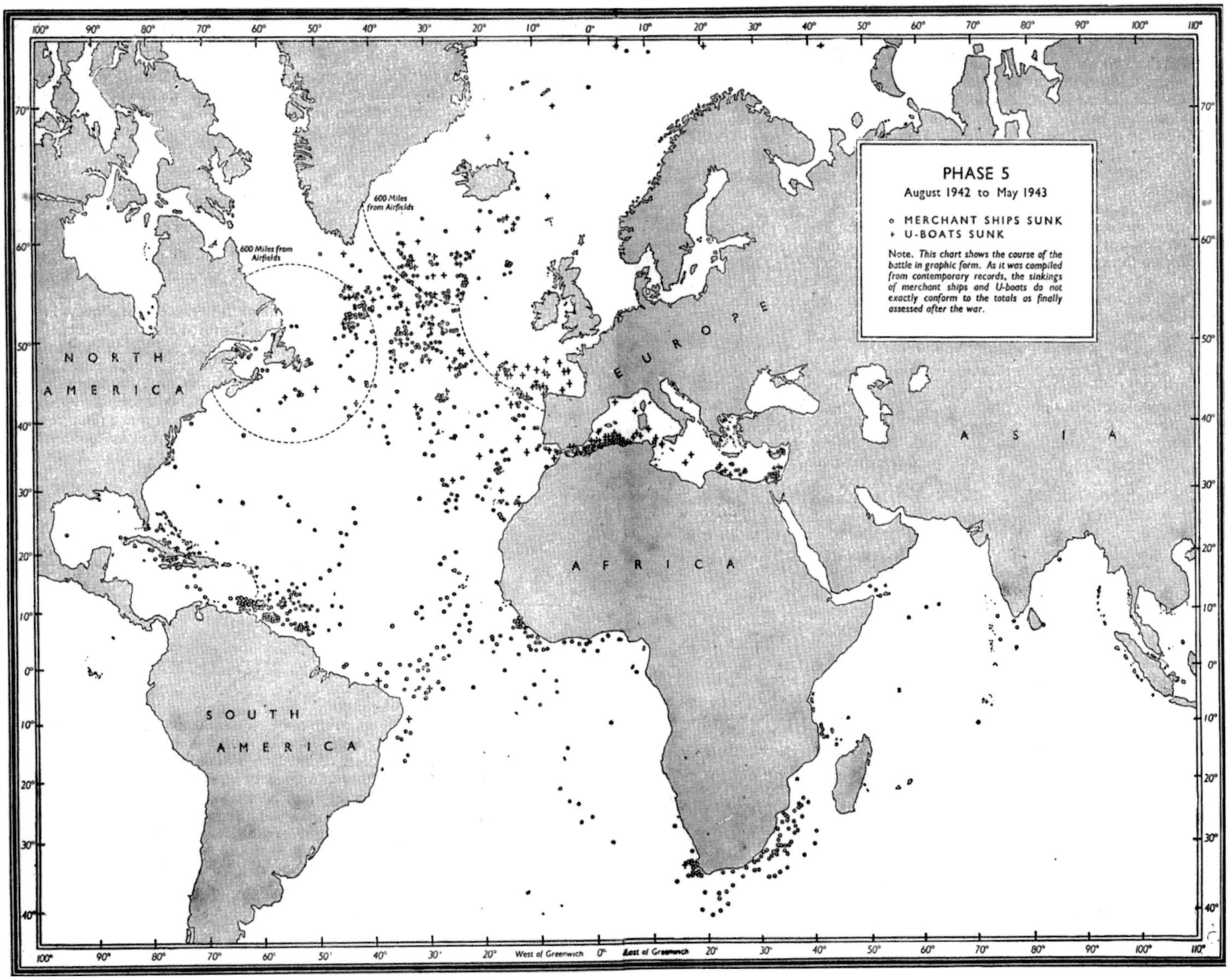

PHASE 5
August 1942 to May 1943
∘ MERCHANT SHIPS SUNK
+ U-BOATS SUNK
Note. This chart shows the course of the battle in graphic form. As it was compiled from contemporary records, the sinkings of merchant ships and U-boats do not exactly conform to the totals as finally assessed after the war.
NORTH AMERICA
SOUTH AMERICA
EUROPE
AFRICA
ASIA
600 Miles from Airfields
600 Miles from Airfields
West of Greenwich
East of Greenwich

Phase 5 of the Atlantic battle. Air cover had improved and the great convoy battles of spring 1943 were mainly fought in the Gap, out of range of aircraft. There were an encouraging number of U-boat sinkings in the Bay of Biscay.

together, while group coordination was aided by the increasing use of TBS voice radio. The lack of such training showed at first among USN groups and also in Home Fleet destroyers detached to act as support groups. With initial warning from HF/DF, location by radar and a coordinated counterattack, the U-boats were finding night surface attack to be much less attractive. Their problems were compounded by the decision to cut training times for captains and crew in order to man the numerous U-boats entering service. From the outbreak of war up to January 1943, 160 U-boats had been lost and each loss meant the loss of not only a qualified commanding officer but also one or more potential COs from the other officers. It required both skill and determination to attack a heavily defended convoy. An example is the attack on convoy SC118 in February 1943. Twenty U-boats were involved, sinking eleven ships (60,000 tons) and damaging one. However, of the twenty U-boats deployed, only three attacked (15 per cent), six of the sinkings being due to one U-boat (U-402, von Forstner). There was also a lack of skilled hydrophone operators.

The U-boat force was still plagued with torpedo problems. An investigation of results in the first six months of 1942 showed that only 404 ships sank, out of 806 hits. This was blamed on the lack of a reliable magnetic fuse, as a torpedo with such a fuse would be certain to sink a merchant ship with a single hit. A new magnetic fuse entered service in late 1942. At about the same date a new electric torpedo, T3, and a pattern runner, G7a FAT, entered service. The scene was set for some of the biggest convoy battles of the war.

Table 6.1: Causes of U-boat sinkings, August 1942–May 1943	
Surface vessels	53
Aircraft	8
Submarine	5
Mines	4
Accident and unknown	8

The Great Convoy Battles of Spring 1943

This book does not attempt to provide a complete history of these great battles. The intention here is to show how new technology and training worked together to contribute to the outcome.

The New Year of 1943 began very badly. On 3 January an all-tanker convoy (TM1) from Trinidad to North Africa was sighted by U-514, which sank one ship before losing contact. Dönitz moved a group of U-boats to intercept and contact was regained on 8 January. This valuable convoy was weakly escorted – one destroyer and three corvettes – some or all having problems with their radar. Altogether, seven of the nine tankers were sunk, earning Dönitz a telegram of congratulations from General von Arnim, commanding German forces in Tunisia. The Casablanca Conference started a week later and this disaster may well have concentrated their minds.

HX231

An insight into the grim struggle that was being played out in mid-Atlantic in the spring of 1943 can be gleaned from the story of convoy HX231. Most of the convoy sailed from New York on 25 March. There was some interchange off Halifax, giving a total of sixty-one ships for the ocean passage. This was one of the largest convoys sailed up to that time and occupied a space six miles wide and two deep. The escort consisted of Escort Group B7 and was very weak for this period of the war. The leader, *Duncan*, was refitting, so her captain (Gretton) took command of the group in the frigate *Tay*. Then there was the 'long-range' V&W destroyer *Vidette* and four Flower class corvettes.[2] The capability of the escort was further reduced by the lack of a rescue ship. This meant that it might be necessary to detach a scarce escort to carry out rescue duties. It also meant that there was only one HF/DF set (*Tay*), precluding the use of cross-bearings to locate an attacker. A support group joined later.

Initially, on 1 April, fifteen U-boats were deployed in a line 200 miles long, twenty miles apart, to locate the convoy. One was lost before joining, but on 1 April six more were directed to the attack. At this date B-Dienst were reading British navy cipher without much delay, while Bletchley Park was yet to master four-rotor Enigma. There were indications at midday on 3 April that the convoy had been sighted, while *Tay*, *Vidette* and *Pink* were able to refuel from the tanker *British Ardour*.

Contact was finally established early on 4 April by U-530 and the U-boats were ordered to attack that night. *Tay* picked up the sighting report and estimated it as close on the port beam. *Vidette* was sent to investigate but failed to make contact. German records show that U-530 was forced to dive at this time, so *Vidette* had some success. By midday, two more U-boats had made sighting reports, both intercepted by *Tay*. The U-boats both say they were forced to dive, but no positive action had been taken so they must have been forced down by routine sweeps.

At 1451, a strong signal was identified and *Vidette* was sent to investigate. She sighted a conning tower fifty minutes later (U-594). By 1630, she had radar contact at 6,000 yards, and soon after that the U-boat dived. Some time later, she had asdic contact and dropped a fourteen pattern, which caused some damage. A later Hedgehog pattern scored no hits and she was recalled. *Alisma* was pursuing another HF/DF report and sighted the U-boat, which dived. By nightfall, five U-boats were in firm contact and others were close.

It was anticipated that the attack would be on the surface, downwind and down-sea, so the escort was concentrated on the port side. Only

Pink was on the starboard side and *Vidette* was still trying to catch up. Both asdic and radar were working on all six ships – somewhat unusual reliability. The weather reduced the performance of both sensors; radar detection was down to about 3,000–4,000 yards.

Just after dark, the convoy altered course 45° to port, returning at 2300 (three hours at eight knots and 45° equates to 5.5 miles off track). The first torpedo hit at 2208 without previous indication. While the convoy was returning to the original course, another ship was torpedoed but was able to maintain convoy speed. The vicinity was illuminated, which seems to have deterred two more submarines from attacking. Unusually, the U-boats were not signalling their intention to attack, as no close signals were picked up by the HF/DF. *Snowflake* made an asdic contact at 0127 on 5 April and dropped a ten pattern on U-572 without inflicting any harm. Three ships decided that the convoy itself was dangerous. One rejoined next day; the other two were sunk, together with a tanker that was straggling because of engine trouble. It was straggling that was suicidal, notwithstanding the fact that U-boat Command criticised submarine commanders for taking the easy option of attacking stragglers rather than the convoy itself. HF/DF reports were now coming in and it would seem that some boats were deterred by the almost random movements of escorts.

At 0228, *Alisma* made another contact on radar at 2,000 yards, which dived and was picked up by asdic. A ten pattern caused serious damage to U-564, which had to return to Lorient. Just before dawn, *Vidette* was moved from station astern to ahead of the convoy in case there were submerged boats planning a dawn attack; there were not. The escort commander was quite pleased with the result; one merchant ship sunk and one damaged was moderate in light of the number of U-boats in contact.

Soon after dawn on 5 April, the convoy was ordered to make an alteration in course, mainly to bring the convoy closer to air support from Iceland (see map). An ambitious air plan had been intended, though emphasising sweeps rather than the more effective escort role. As a result of bad weather and homing problems, much of this support failed to materialise and the first Liberator only arrived just after midday. It immediately sighted U-584 and dropped six depth charges. The submarine was not sunk as was then thought, but played no further part in the battle. U-260 was in the vicinity, too, and dived to avoid air attack.

U-706 had lost contact during the night but the alteration of course brought it into a fine attacking position. She fired two torpedoes, one

The American-built Captain class began to enter service in 1943, but none took part in the great convoy battles of that Spring. This is *Keats*, a diesel-engined Captain, probably during work up.

of them hitting the escort tanker *British Ardour*, which sank later. Because of poor weather conditions, the attacker was not located. By about 1330, a second Liberator had joined and for about three hours not one signal was intercepted, an indication that the aircraft had forced all U-boats to submerge. The aircraft left at about 1710 and very soon HF/DF began to receive messages – and there were three hours of daylight still to go.

There were still twenty U-boats targeted on the convoy, although not many were in contact. It was decided to repeat the successful diversion of the previous night – 30° to port just after dark, 40° starboard three hours later. For most of the night, the convoy was heading east with wind from south to south-west, so attacks were most likely from the starboard side, at least after the second turn.

The escort commander expected to receive warning of imminent attacks from HF/DF and told his ships that there could be no sustained attacks on a U-boat with the danger of leaving a gap in the screen; just one quick pattern and rejoin. At 2012, U-594 inadvertently surfaced in the middle of the convoy. The CO decided he was too close to fire torpedoes and escaped ahead, where he was picked up on radar by *Alisma*. The U-boat dived and *Alisma* dropped a scaring pattern. While she was rejoining, a second contact was made and attacked with a ten pattern. Gretton thinks that this may have been the end of U-635.

Loosestrife made a radar contact at 2120. It was one of those times when everything possible went wrong – lack of reports, wrong setting on the depth charges, etc. Soon after, *Tay*'s HF/DF picked up more signals and *Pink* made radar contact with U-270. A ten pattern caused slight damage. Another contact was made by the watchful *Alisma* at 2150. Then there was a lull until *Pink* obtained a radar contact and fired starshell, driving off the attacker.

The second turn was completed at about midnight. At about the same time, HF/DF detected a contact on the starboard bow and escorts were alerted. *Tay* sighted a U-boat crossing her bows only 150 yards away. *Tay* could not match the U-boat's turning circle; the guns could not train fast enough and the 4in got off only one round. The U-boat dived at 800 yards and was soon picked up by asdic, whereupon a 'good' fourteen pattern was dropped. *Tay* ran out to 1,000 yards and made contact close to the original explosion. Sounds as of blowing tanks followed by a heavy explosion were heard, with a red glow seen by *Tay*'s lookouts. The Assessment Committee awarded a kill but study of records after the war makes this unlikely. Gretton compares the verdicts of the Admiralty U-Boat Assessment Committee with German records and finds their judgement to be very accurate overall.

There were numerous reports from HF/DF but the next contact was not till 0310, when *Alisma* made radar contact at 2,000 yards. The U-boat dived and *Alisma* attacked, making a rare mistake as only seven charges of her ten pattern dropped. This may have been the end of U-635, whose fate is uncertain. At 0415, *Pink* made radar contact at the very long range of 4,800 yards. Visual contact was made at 800 yards but asdic contact was lost (probably the determined U-706). There was a HF/DF warning at 0425 of two boats ahead of the convoy, but only U-134 closed and she was unable to reach a firing position because of the unconscious movements of the escorts. At 0500, a merchant ship damaged earlier had to be abandoned as her bulkheads failed.

During the night at least ten and possibly as many as sixteen attacks had been beaten off without further losses. Considering that there were twenty U-boats deployed, this shows how difficult it had become to attack even a lightly protected convoy. They were kept down by aircraft during the day, so that it was difficult to reach an attacking position, while night attack on the surface was almost impossible against centimetric radar. General morale in the U-boat force was still good but attacks were just too difficult for these inexperienced COs.

The morning of 6 April was filthy, with high wind and sea from the south-west, low cloud and visibility down to less than two miles. There were grounds for optimism, since the support group was expected to join soon, as were aircraft. The escort commander did not expect that submarines could maintain contact in such weather but he was wrong; several did keep in contact using their excellent hydrophones. U-boat Command sent an ill-judged signal telling its boats to attack with more determination; it did not help.

The day's first action began at 0647, when *Tay*'s asdic operator reported a submarine contact at 900 yards on the port bow. His report was not at first believed but he stuck with it and was proved right, for which he was decorated. It was U-270; as she dived her stern was seen coming out of the water. A shallow ten pattern was ordered but only five charges dropped. It was three hours before U-270 surfaced.

At about 0800, the first Liberator arrived after a difficult four-hour flight. Two more joined shortly after, giving powerful assistance. The support group of four Home Fleet destroyers also joined about this time.[3] There was a potential problem, in that the support group commander was senior in rank to the commander of the escort group. Western Approaches rules were that the escort group commander, in close touch with the situation, remained in charge. Thanks to the tact of both officers, there was no clash on this occasion. The support group were lacking in convoy experience but welcome additions to the screen, particularly as two had HF/DF. For no apparent reason, none of the three HF/DF with the escort picked up any signal all day, although shore stations intercepted

plenty of signals from the area of the convoy.

The lack of HF/DF reception meant that it was not possible to direct the aircraft on to specific targets but they did very well on their own. At 0942, an aircraft attacked U-584, causing damage that forced her to return home. Shortly after, another aircraft inflicted severe damage on U-592. The first wave of aircraft were relieved by others, and one of these made an attack at 1618 that probably accounted for U-632. The last aircraft left at 1935. Though some eight U-boats remained in contact using hydrophones, there were no attacks during the night. U-boat Command instructed the remaining boats to overtake the convoy during the night and attack submerged at daybreak. A considerable number of HF/DF interceptions were made in the course of the night.

It was the RAF's day. There was an escort of Liberators and a supporting sweep of four Fortresses. The sweep made one unsuccessful attack but did locate a lifeboat with survivors. A Liberator reached the convoy at 0805, after all-too-common homing problems. It sighted a U-boat (now known to be U-463) at 0919 and dropped four charges.[4] Another aircraft attacked at 1234, causing no damage; the same aircraft sighted a U-boat while on the way home and, having no depth charges left, attacked with machine guns, forcing the boat to dive. The next aircraft pursued a HF/DF contact at 1710 and dropped five charges. This was the last attack but

There were two variants of the Captain class, a diesel-engined version and a slightly larger and faster type with turbines. The first into service were diesel vessels like *Mounsey*, seen here in 1944.

the aircraft remained till dark. There were a few contacts on HF/DF during the night but these died down as U-boat Command stopped the operation.

The tally was two U-boats sunk for three merchant ships sunk in convoy and three stragglers. At first sight, this may seem much like a draw but this view would be mistaken; the vast majority of the ships and their valuable cargoes reached their destination safely. This was success.

There were lessons to be drawn from the events surrounding convoy HX231. The following discussion blends the escort group commander's contemporary views with the author's hindsight.

In many of the individual actions, there is a common pattern. First detection would be by HF/DF, giving at least a general alert of submarines in contact. Usually this contact would locate the transmitter either to a point, given two or more sets, or to a line of bearing, with only one set as in *Tay*. Such contacts would lead to the need for speed in a proportion of the escorts to run down the bearing, pursue the contact and return to their station. Centimetric radar of the 271 series made night surface attack almost impossible – certainly for inexperienced U-boat COs.

The importance of training both as individuals and as a group was reinforced. A part of the brief period between runs needed to be devoted to training. Even basics such as depth charge drill still needed practice. Conversely, the U-boat arm was reducing training time – and it showed.

Methods of dealing with a surfaced submarine at close range needed a lot of attention (see later sections on ramming, 'Shark',

etc.). The need for a rescue ship and the danger of straggling were already well-known lessons.

Conversely, the value of unpredictable movements by escorts had not been appreciated. Nervous U-boat captains would keep their heads down. U-boats and their commanding officers were not lacking in courage, but by 1943 an attack on a convoy, either by day or night, was too difficult for these inexperienced officers. Gretton points out that of the twenty deployed against HX231, two were killed during the action, twelve more were killed before the war ended and only six of the twenty survived.

The value of milch cows was recognised but only if contact could be made without giving away the position.

Air escort was invaluable. If U-boats were kept down all day, they could not get ahead of the convoy for a later attack. Homing procedures and communication with aircraft needed improvement, as did their depth charge drill; there were too many hang-ups.

Many of these lessons were already well known by 1943, thanks very largely to the 'wash up' meeting after each convoy. There followed a series of similar encounters (see table 6.2).

ONS5

ONS5 was a slow, westbound convoy of forty-two ships. The escort was Group B7, recovered from the battle for HX231. The group commander, Gretton, was back in his own destroyer, *Duncan*. The corvette *Alisma*, which had done so well in HX231, had gone for a much-needed refit and was replaced by *Sunflower*. Two rescue trawlers were a most welcome addition. There were two refuelling oilers but one proved useless as it had canvas hoses, which broke,

Table 6.2: Some critical convoys of April 1943			
Convoy	**Ships lost (stragglers)**	**U-boats sunk**	**Departure**
HX232	3	?	1 April
HX233	1	1	6 April
SC126	0	0	8 April
HX234	1 (1)	1	12 April
ONS4	0	2	13 April
SC127	0	0	16 April
HX235	0	1	18 April
ONS5	11 (2)	7	21 April

Spragge, a turbine Captain: note the shield on B gun.

instead of rubber. The escort met the convoy in the North Channel on 22 April. The first two days were marked by worsening weather, which increased to gale force causing two ships to collide, one of which had to make its way to Iceland for repairs, without escort.

On the 24th a Fortress sank U-710, which was lying ahead of the convoy. The weather improved a little on the 27th, allowing *Duncan* and *Vidette* to refuel. The next day, a close signal was picked up on HF/DF and it was clear that the convoy had been spotted and reported. U-650 was able to shadow all day and fourteen more U-boats were ordered to join the attack. Several sweeps down HF/DF bearings were without success. At 1830, *Duncan* and *Tay* made a visual sighting but the submarine dived and could not be picked up by asdic. At nightfall, there was a strong wind and sea from the port quarter, so the escort force was concentrated in that area. This placing proved sound; *Sunflower*

beat off the first attack on the port bow by U-386, causing some damage; *Duncan* foiled four on the port quarter and *Snowflake* countered another on the port beam. It had been a good night, with no losses in the convoy and one or two U-boats damaged.

However, early on the morning of the 29th, U-258 penetrated the screen from ahead and sank one ship, escaping without detection. On the 30th, a number of contacts were attacked without result. *Oribi,* the first of the 3rd Escort Group to join in support, arrived that night. There were no attacks overnight, mainly because of the severe weather. The conditions caused the convoy to scatter but Liberators did a great job in directing lost sheep back to the convoy. By nightfall there were thirty-two ships in the main body, while *Pink* was looking after a further four a few miles away.

That night the rest of the support group joined, making five destroyers.[5] The weather was still too bad for refuelling and *Duncan* had to leave the convoy, arriving at St Johns with tanks almost empty,[6] leaving the command to Lt Cdr Sherwood in *Tay*. Three of the support group destroyers soon followed.

Dönitz had set up a force of thirty U-boats to attack SC128, which passed the submarine line without being sighted. The U-boats were only eight miles apart and it must have been the weather that saved SC128. However, ONS5 was picked up on 4 May to the surprise of both sides. The weather and the distance from bases made close air support impossible but an RCAF 'Canso'[7] spotted U-630 ahead of the convoy and sank her. There were many intercepted signals that day and some visual sightings, but no attacks during the day. The night was a different story. Six merchant ships were sunk, keeping the rescue trawlers, *Northern Gem* and *Northern Spray*, busy and proving their worth.

At daybreak on 5 May, the escort in company comprised two destroyers of the support group, *Oribi* and *Offa*, one destroyer (*Vidette*) of the escort group, a frigate (*Tay*) and three corvettes, *Pink*, *Sunflower* and *Snowflake*. The weather had moderated enough to permit some refuelling but during the day four more of the convoy were sunk. *Pink*'s little group lost a ship, but *Pink* sank U-192 . The grim situation was relieved only by the promise of the 1st Escort Group's joining in a day or two.

On the night of 5/6 May, fifteen U-boats were available to attack but fog made visual observation difficult for them, giving the advantage to the radar-equipped escorts. They beat off twenty-five attacks without loss, while four U-boats were sunk or seriously damaged. The next morning, Dönitz called off the attack. In all, thirteen merchant ships had been sunk, but aircraft in support of the convoy had sunk two U-boats, the 1st Escort Group on the way to join had sunk another, and five were sunk by the escort. In addition, two U-boats collided, both sinking. Ten U-boats in one convoy battle – a great, but little-known, victory. There were still two more years of war to come but the U-boat was never again a potential winner.

The main lesson of ONS5 was the need for sufficient endurance in escort vessels. In the interim, better equipment and procedures for oiling at sea were needed. The effect of the weather on the operational capability of both escorts and submarines was also clearly seen.

Also in May, HX237 lost three stragglers but two U-boats were sunk. SC129 lost three ships and sank two U-boats (one Liberator using the Mk 24 mine).

On 24 May 1943, Dönitz ordered the U-boats to withdraw from the North Atlantic.

Technical Developments

It is hard to attribute any particular development to this short period, so the opportunity will be taken to outline two aspects that were of concern throughout the war.

Surfaced Submarines

It was – is – not easy to sink a surfaced submarine even if it was disabled. Only a small arc of the circular pressure hull would be exposed to gunfire, and the impact of a shell would be at such an oblique angle that it would glance off the tough plating without penetration.

In the early years of the war, ramming was seen as a more certain kill. A study in May 1943 showed that of twenty-seven rammings, twenty-four led to the submarine's sinking. In roughly half the cases considered, the submarine had been severely damaged by depth charges. Ramming an undamaged submarine was not easy, as the turning circle of a U-boat was less than that of most escorts (see chapter 8, table 8.10). Accounts describe a number of unsuccessful attempts to ram but overall figures are not available.

C-in-C Western Approaches was asked what speed was needed for a successful ramming. He replied that fourteen knots was too slow and suggested twenty knots (a speed that many escorts could not reach!). The Director of Naval Construction was asked the same question and replied that the higher speed the better. Damage to the attacking ship was inevitable but did not increase greatly with speed of impact.

Damage was usually serious, with the lower bow wrecked back to, and including, the asdic dome. It is hard to give a precise time for repairs, as other much-needed work would be undertaken while the ship was available, but seven to eight weeks was typical. (It seemed that repairs took five and a half weeks after ramming a damaged U-boat and eight and a half for an intact one.) In at least one case, a destroyer ran over her victim, disabling both shafts in the process, and was later torpedoed while stationary. At least one other ship lost a single shaft.

These figures led to an interesting operational research comparison.[8] It was found that an escort vessel saved two to three merchant ships per year, so that loss of service during repairs after ramming equated to 0.4 merchant ships sunk. On the other hand, sinking a U-boat corresponded to saving fourteen merchant ships. This crude analysis shows that ramming was most cost-effective.

However, damage to escorts was to be avoided if possible. By the end of 1942 a fuse setting was available for depth charges to explode at fifteen feet. With Torpex filling, the lethal radius was about twenty feet, which made feasible the use of depth charges against surfaced submarines. Ramming was not forbidden but from early 1943 was firmly discouraged.

Other means were tried. During 1944 a number of escorts had Oerlikons in the bridge wings replaced by ancient 6pdrs (see appendix II).

From late 1943 a number of escorts were given ancient 6pdrs in the bridge wings to use against surfaced submarines, as in this photo of the corvette *Snowflake*. There is no record of success.

Apparently it was thought that the main gun, 4in or more, was too slow to train, but nevertheless the chance of a 6pdr shot holing a submarine seems remote. No example of its use has been found.

Shark

The problem of sinking surfaced U-boats was appreciated and a special projectile, the Shark, was devised, to be fired from a 4in gun. The complete projectile weighed 96lb, was 73.66in long and was fired with a muzzle velocity of 500ft/sec. It was intended to be fired at fairly short range and enter the water short of the submarine. Spoiler rings on the nose helped preserve the trajectory underwater. There was a hardened-steel nose (33lb), which would pierce both ballast tanks and pressure hull before the charge of 24lb of Torpex exploded.

In Operation 'Deadlight'[9] six Sharks were fired against U-3514 (Type XXI) at a range of 2,400 feet. The last two hit and the submarine sank in about a minute.

Camouflage[10]

In 1939 all Home Fleet ships were painted dark grey, as major warships had been since Victorian black and white was abandoned in 1904. Destroyers remained all black until late in 1915, in the mistaken view that black was 'invisible' at night. Once the Second World War broke out,

various schemes of camouflage were adopted, very much on a 'do it yourself' basis. C-in-C Western Approaches (Dunbar-Nasmith) was an enthusiast and encouraged such initiatives, starting with the destroyers *Grenville* and *Grenade* in 1939.

Early in 1940, Lt Peter Scott, RNVR was serving in the destroyer *Broke*, for which he devised a special paint scheme. Peter Scott was not only a keen yachtsman, as were many RNVR officers, but a well-known artist specialising in paintings of water birds, which gave him an understanding of Nature's camouflage. The C-in-C liked Scott's design and asked him to design a paint scheme for the ex-American Town class. This became the basis for the 'Western Approaches Scheme', though it did not become official until April 1942.[11]

Scott was insistent that a camouflage scheme would be effective in one condition of lighting only and there should be no compromise. He chose minimum visibility from a surfaced U-boat at night and, to many people's surprise, a basically white scheme. To break up the outlines there were panels of very pale blue and green. Later in the war, green pigments were scarce and some ships had blue panels only. His aim was to ensure that all parts of a ship that could be seen from a conning tower were pale in colour. In bright sunshine or moonlight the ships might be a little more visible in consequence, although the scheme worked well at dawn and dusk. It was found that Scott's patterns were also effective against aerial observation, although sightings by aircraft were usually of the wake.

Western Approaches painting was used by a number of ships not in that command, eg Hunt class destroyers, *Halcyon* class minesweepers and some trawlers. Wartime paints had a simple oil base and did not adhere well in Atlantic seas, particularly when applied to wet or dirty surfaces, and model-makers interested in the period are recommended to incorporate a generous measure of 'rust' in their work.

There is no way of telling how effective this paint scheme was in the U-boat war. Certainly, there are plenty of reports that ships so painted were harder to see but usually there was no basis for comparison. It may be that the value was mainly psychological, crews feeling that something had been done to make them invisible.

Captain Class Frigates (American DE)

The concept of these ships had two starting points: USN views on a cheap destroyer and the somewhat differing views of the RN on an ocean escort. The early studies showed that rate at which a cheap version of a first-line warship under design loses capability is much greater than that at which cost is reduced. Even the might of US industry was overstretched and the design of the DEs was heavily constrained by limits on machinery and weapon supply. Despite these problems, the several groups of destroyer escorts form the most numerous class of warships ever built – and a very effective class.

The USN Studies[12]

Until about 1937, the USN had no requirement for a cheap vessel of destroyer type. There were a large number of the old 'flush deck' type for ocean escort, supported by PC boats for coastal work. By 1939, there were doubts as to whether the big fleet destroyers could be built rapidly in the numbers thought to be needed and proposals were made for a simpler vessel. An armament of four guns (3-, 4- or 5-inch) with forty-eight depth charges and a speed of twenty-five knots was envisaged. Endurance of about 6,000 miles at twelve knots and good sea-keeping were required and it was hoped to keep the displacement under 1,200 tons.

The *Farragut*s were only 1,400 tons, so 1,200 seemed a reasonable target; but it was not to be, mainly because the older ship did not have unitised machinery. The Bureau of Construction and Repair argued for more ships of the 1,630 class, on the basis that there would be savings in lead time. The introduction of a new class will always need considerable investment in drawings, mock-ups, tooling, etc. In addition, some of the knowledge gained in building an earlier class will be irrelevant and experience will have to be built up on the new design (the 'learning curve'). In the summer of 1940, Gibbs and Cox prepared a design study and President Roosevelt wanted four prototypes built. Adm Stark (CNO) joined in with an all-too-common demand for a much heavier armament on a

Right, above and below: Aylmer, a turbine Captain. Note the addition of an RN whaler in the later picture (below).

smaller ship, just as the Bureau began to think that 1,200 tons was insufficient for the lighter armament. Several schemes were tried but the most promising was estimated to cost $6.8 million, as against $8.1 million for a 1,630-ton first-rate destroyer. By February 1941, the most favoured scheme was Study B, a ship of 1,125 tons (standard), with a speed of twenty-four knots and mounting two 5in/38-calibre guns.

Cochrane and the British Connection

The head of preliminary design in the Bureau of Ships (BuShips) was now Capt E L Cochrane. He had been to the UK for some time in the autumn of 1940, studying British ideas. He was made welcome by the DNC, Sir Stanley Goodall, who had been attached to the Bureau of Construction and Repair during World War I, where he had met Cochrane. Cochrane liked the British Hunt class, although he realised that they were not suitable for USN purposes because of their short endurance. He picked up ideas such as an open bridge on A/S ships and the value of torpedo tubes (fitted in the Type III Hunt class) as a weapon against surface attack.

On 23 June 1941, the British delegation in Washington sent a formal request to the Secretary of the Navy for 100 escort destroyers. Outline requirements were for a speed of at least twenty knots, a length of 300 feet (for good sea-keeping), a dual-purpose gun armament and an open bridge. The DE design seemed very much what was wanted, although there was some opposition on the grounds that a British programme of DEs might cause delays to the USN programme of fleet destroyers. When the USA entered the war, the RN programme was subsumed into that of the USN. In total, seventy-eight DEs were lent to the RN. In fact, the great majority of both RN and USN DEs were built in yards not involved in destroyer-building. In all, 1,005 ships were authorised for the USN and allies. In the spring of 1944, this was cut back to 600 and later to 565. The number actually

Lawson, a diesel-engined Captain, was another ship with a shield on B gun. This was the only gun manned during cruising watches, giving the crew a modicum of shelter. It also enabled rocket flares to be used from launchers mounted on the sides of the gun-shield.

completed was 498, of which 306 completed by the end of 1943. It was a wonderful achievement.

There were, however, real bottlenecks in the supply of major items of equipment. It was intended that all DEs should mount two 5in/38-calibre dual-purpose guns and all had the stability (beam) to carry these guns. However, the weapon was in short supply and priority was understandably given to major warships and, later, to USN DEs. The DEs had only limited fire control equipment and even the excellent 5in gun would not have been very effective in AA fire. All early DEs, RN and USN, completed with three 3in/50-calibre guns. These were of little value in either AA or A/S use, as their shells were unlikely to penetrate the tough and well-rounded pressure hull of a U-boat. This armament was lighter than that intended and contributed to the excessive metacentric height, making them unduly stiff and leading to their rolling problems (see chapter 8).

Machinery was an even bigger problem. It had been originally envisaged that they would have twin-shaft, geared turbines with a total of 12,000shp, but there was a shortage of gear-cutting machinery. Gear cutters are complicated machines; it would be some time before they were available and an alternative machinery plant was needed. There seemed to be a solution in the diesel-electric plant used in USN submarines, where each shaft had two 1,500bhp General Motors V-12 diesels driving generators to a 3,000hp electric motor. Four diesels per shaft would provide the power needed for a fast DE from well-proven units. Fitting diesels meant lengthening the ship by three and a half feet and an increase of 130 tons in displacement. However, it was subsequently realised that the diesels, too, were in short supply and consequently it was decided to fit only two diesels per shaft for a combined total of 6,000bhp and a loss of

about four knots in top speed. These became the USN *Evarts* class (GMT – GM Tandem Diesel). Thirty-two of these ships were lent to the RN.

The next group of DEs had 12,000shp turbine machinery driving through generators and electric motors, which added twenty feet to the length, two feet to the beam and 200 tons to the displacement; the extra length was beneficial to speed and helped them to reach at least twenty-four knots. Forty-six of these ships (USN *Buckley* class TE[13]) served in the RN.

The earlier groups of DEs had the open bridge desired by the RN, with an asdic hut let into the forward side. The hull was flush-decked with considerable sheer to give adequate freeboard forward. They had a long, continuous superstructure from B to X gun. Internally, they were fitted out to USN standards and were far more comfortable than contemporary RN ships, discussed later under the Colony class.

They all mounted three 3in guns, and many had one twin Bofors and upwards of five Oerlikons as completed. The British ships had four depth charge throwers and two rails (ten pattern). They were also given two special rails for launching the 'one ton' depth charge Mk 10. Initially, they had 112 depth charges but this was increased to 160 as part of the measures to reduce roll. By the time they completed, Hedgehog was available and fitted abaft A gun. Type 144 asdic was fitted in most, though some had 128D, which could be updated to 144. A few had Type 147 installed.

They had twin rudders behind the twin propellers at the suggestion of William Hovgaard, which model tests showed reduced the turning circle by some 25 per cent (see chapter 8), very important in depth charge attacks.

The design was developed by Gibbs and Cox, concentrating on ease of production. They were all-welded mild steel, built in prefabricated

Table 6.3: Captain class (as built)	Diesel (32 ships)	Turbine (46 ships)
Displacement, deep, standard (tons):	1,450, 1,150	1,840, 1,300
Dimensions (feet):	289½ x 35 x 10¾	306 x 37 x 12½
Shp and speed (kts):	6,000 = 20	12,000 = 24
Fuel (tons), endurance (miles) @ (kts):	198, 6,000 @ 12	350, 6,000 @ 12
Complement:	198	220

Curzon, a turbine Captain with a very heavy AA armament. As well as the twin Bofors aft she seems to have singles forward of the bridge and at least eight Oerlikons.

sections. The majority of the shell and deck plating was quarter-inch, with half-inch for the garboard strakes. Superstructure bulkheads were only three-sixteenths of an inch. This structure proved largely trouble-free in service. The all-welded hull with its freedom from leaks was welcomed by the crews. Delivery began in January 1943 with the diesel ships ahead of the turbines. A total of 24 entered service in 1943 and 54 in 1944. Table 6.3 shows the technical specifications of the class as built; note the fuel economy of the diesel ships.

RN Modifications[14]

Modifications carried out in RN ships were initially comparatively minor. Torpedo tubes were omitted in all, with the intention (initially not fulfilled) of fitting more anti-aircraft guns. B gun, which was manned in cruising stations, was given a spray shield, enabling rocket flare launchers to be fitted. Many more Oerlikons and some single Bofors were added as they became available. Those ships employed on east coast duties were given a 2pdr pom-pom on the stem as an anti-E-boat weapon. Snowflake flares were fitted on the bridge wings and smoke floats were carried on top of the depth charge rails. Most had a HF/DF aerial at the masthead. A crow's nest was fitted on the mast. A twenty-seven-foot whaler was carried in standard RN luffing davits on the port side. Other additions included oiling fairleads, extra life rafts and improved wind screens.

Other, more extensive modifications were considered but not implemented. The first such scheme involved mounting 4.7in guns in place of 3in. Later ideas involved twin 4in in place of A and X, and 3in with a twin Squid (twenty-four salvoes) in place of B gun, with 144 and 147 asdic. Six twin and four single Oerlikons would be mounted. An AA version would have had three 5in DP guns with a Mk 50 director, three twin Bofors and four single Oerlikons. Only twelve depth charges would be carried, with 128 asdic. Three TE were converted to coastal force control and three GMT to LSH(S). Five were planned for conversion to fighter direction ships. Five others were being converted to floating electrical power stations at the war's end. Of these, *Hotham* was retained, with the intention to use her as a gas-turbine test bed, but this never came about.

It was intended to replace one of *Hotham*'s steam turbines with a gas turbine, leaving steam on the other for comparison, the electric drive making the connection straightforward. The chosen engine was the English Electric EL60A.

Steam turbine technology was employed for long life, making the plant big and heavy. The EL60A ran shore trials in late 1951 but it had become obvious that this was not the way to go and the project was abandoned in 1952. *Hotham* was returned to the USN in 1956 and scrapped.[15]

Five GMT and two TE were lost, and three GMT and seven TE damaged beyond economic repair (presumably because so many new ones were coming into service).

Speed of the Captain Class

There were actually two Captain classes: one with diesel-electric propulsion (GMT) and a speed of twenty knots, the other with steam turbo-electric propulsion and a speed of twenty-four knots (TE), with identical weapon and sensor fit. In their analyses of U-boat sinkings by escort class, both Brown[16] and Collingwood[17] treated the two classes together, noting that the combined total of sinkings was rather higher than would be expected from their equipment (Hedgehog, depth charges and Type 144 asdic). A simple attempt to separate the two classes came up with some interesting statistics: 'The thirty-two diesel ships were involved in nine sinkings, the forty-six steamers in seventeen, with three sinkings involving both types.'

The analysis was crude and included all sinkings – English Channel and Arctic, as well as the main Atlantic battleground. However, the results are consistent with accounts by authors such as Macintyre,[18] who commanded a mixed group of three diesel and three steamers. Almost always, it was a steamship that would be detached to prosecute a target, as the four knots of extra speed reduced the time needed to rejoin.

The difference between the classes becomes even more remarkable when it is noted that five of the diesel ships' seven successes came in 1943 (or January 1944), before many steamers were worked up.

The need for a significant proportion of escorts to have a relatively high speed is clear. Two hours behind a seven-knot convoy takes fifty minutes to catch up at twenty-four knots, sixty-five minutes at twenty knots.

The Colony Class Frigates[19]

In 1942, the USN was anxious to build even more escort vessels. It was thought that some yards in the USA would have difficulty in building DEs, with their more complicated structure, but could build to merchant-ship style. The British River class was selected as the basis for these new ships and the famous design agency

The Colony class, such as *Antigua* shown here, were an American adaptation of the British Rivers. By the time they entered service their technology was dated.

Table 6.4: Colony class
Displacement (tons): 1,509, 2,238 deep
Dimensions (feet): 285½ pp, 304 oa x 37½ x 13¼ deep
Shp and speed (kts): 5,500 = 20 (18 continuous)
Fuel (tons), endurance (miles) @ (kts): 768, 7,300 @ 11; 6,400 @ 14; 5,270 @ 16¼; 3,000 @ 19
Complement: 120

Gibbs and Cox was chosen to develop the design. They were originally designated as gunboats (PG) but in April 1943 all were reclassified as frigates (PF). In all, 100 were ordered, of which twenty-one were transferred to the RN (PF 72–92).

In the redesign, beam was increased by one foot, and two and three-quarters feet added to the length amidships to accommodate the longer US machinery. This consisted of two Babcock and Wilcox three-drum boilers delivering steam at 250psi to two four-cylinder triple-expansion engines. Despite the increase in size, the hull weighed fifty tons less than that of a River, as a result of its all-welded construction.

Armament consisted of three 3in guns, four 40mm Bofors and six single Oerlikons. They had a Hedgehog, four depth charge throwers and two rails, with US Navy SA (air warning) and SL (surface) radars. Late in the war, it was proposed to convert the whole class to air warning ships, for which role they would have had a Type 277 set aft and a fighter direction office at the foot of the foremast. Only *Caicos* completed the conversion.

The twenty-one British ships formed the total output of the Walsh-Kaiser yard at Providence, Rhode Island. Virtually the whole class suffered severe machinery problems on build. Monsarrat states that his ship was delayed for eight months by these problems, running fourteen sets of trials.[20] Whatever the problem was, the cure seems to have been complete, as there were few complaints after the vessels' entry into service.

The USN had three areas of concern, reviewed by Johnson.[21] They were said to be

Dominica, another Colony. By British standards they were luxuriously equipped.

It was intended to fit the whole Colony class as air warning ships for the Pacific but only *Caicos* was completed as such. Note the 277 aerial abaft the mainmast.

structurally weak, which seems unlikely. They did suffer from cracking at the numerous sharp corners of openings, which would spread easily in their welded structure. They had a much larger turning circle than the DEs, with twin rudders. Finally, they were said to have inadequate ventilation, a complaint upheld by Johnson, who served in PF 40. This seems unlikely in the light of the RN plans to convert them for Pacific duties. Perhaps the USN views on ventilation differed from those of the RN, where the louvres were often stuffed with an old pair of socks!

On the other hand, the RN crews were delighted with their 'luxurious' accommodation. Monsarrat gives a most interesting comparison when the crew of a River were transferred en bloc to a Colony.[22] The

equipment to USN standards included a laundry (*Warrior* had a laundry in 1860), ice-water dispensers in each mess deck, dish washers, potato peelers, ice cream machines, typewriters and two cinema projectors. There was an internal communication system with loudspeakers in each mess deck and a telephone system with an exchange. There were no voice pipes – the captain had a microphone round his neck. None of this impinged on safety: the furniture was all-metal, there were no rugs or linoleum and the few door curtains were of fibre glass. There were no side scuttles.

Deliveries began late in 1943, by which time their A/S equipment was dated and U-boats were scarce. They may be seen as a little better than a River but inferior to the Lochs. They claimed two and a half sinkings.

7 Pause, Counterattack and Victory:
June 1943–May 1945

When Dönitz withdrew his U-boats from the North Atlantic in June 1943, he decided to deploy them against the routes used to reinforce the US forces in North Africa from the States. It was not a wise decision, as the USN used five escort carriers in the area, accounting for sixteen U-boats for the loss of only six ships from convoys. Another mistake was to order U-boats to cross the Bay of Biscay in groups on the surface by day, a decision that cost twenty-nine U-boats as the obvious counter of aircraft also working in groups was introduced. By the beginning of August, it was realised that the Metox radar detector was ineffective, and a new detector proved no better since it still did not recognise the 10-centimetre radar that was being used. Dönitz changed the transit rules, with boats crossing the bay independently, surfacing only by night to charge batteries and hugging the Spanish coast to confuse aircraft radar. Sinking in the bay transit dropped dramatically to about one per month.

Withdrawal from the principal North Atlantic convoy routes was intended to be only temporary, pending the introduction of new technology. Existing submarines were to have their AA armament greatly increased and, more importantly, they were to be equipped with torpedoes that would home on the noise from escort vessels' propellers. New types of submarine were to be brought forward – first the fast battery boats, Types XXI and XXIII, and then the much faster hydrogen peroxide boats of Walter design.

The tonnage of merchant ships sunk was below 100,000, except in July (238,000). The total number of U-boats was fairly constant, at about 429. Roughly half were available for operations, the remainder being on trials or training. These figures equated to some fifty tons sunk per U-boat-day at sea.

Table 7.1: Causes of U-boat sinkings, June–September 1943	
Surface vessels	16½
Aircraft	64½
Submarine	2
Mines	1
Accident and unknown	5

As can be seen from table 7.1, the outstanding feature of the period was the number of sinkings due to aircraft. This was partly a result of Dönitz's ill-considered policy of fighting on the surface and crossing the Bay of Biscay in groups, but probably owed more to better aircraft, better weapons and better training.

From Counterattack to Victory: October 1943–May 1945

By September 1943, Dönitz felt confidence in the U-boats' ability to re-enter the Atlantic battle. They had enhanced anti-aircraft armament and a new radar detector (Wanz) to protect them from air attack, and the new homing torpedo (T5) with which they could strike against surface escorts. The first big test came on 20 September 1943, when twenty-two

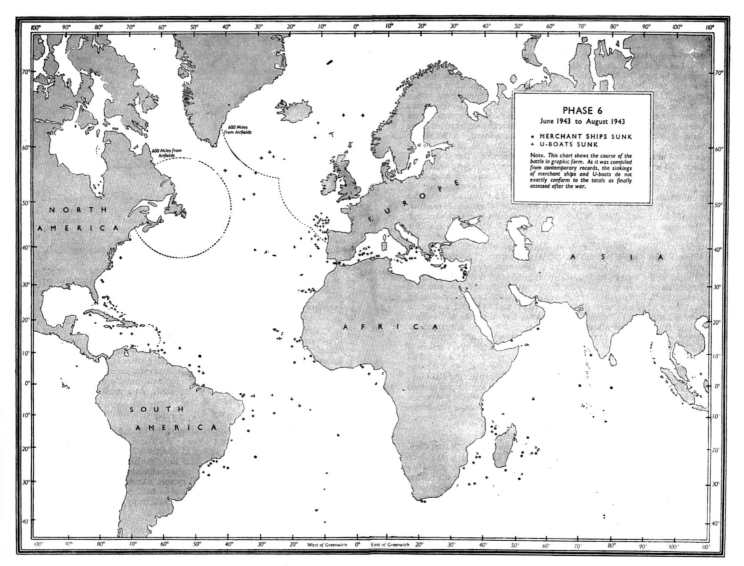

PHASE 6
June 1943 to August 1943

• MERCHANT SHIPS SUNK
+ U-BOATS SUNK

Note. This chart shows the course of the battle in graphic form. As it was compiled from contemporary records, the sinkings of merchant ships and U-boats do not exactly conform to the totals as finally assessed after the war.

Phase 6 of the Atlantic battle. The lack of merchantmen sinkings shows that the battle had been won. The Bay of Biscay was a major killing ground with many U-boats destroyed.

U-boats launched an attack on the combined forces of ON202 and ONS18. By the time action was broken off because of fog on the 23rd, six merchant ships totalling 36,000 tons had been sunk, as had three U-boats.

The attack on the escorts had interesting consequences. Twenty-four T5 torpedoes had been fired and it was claimed that twelve escorts had been sunk, with three more probables. This claimed figure was about what had been expected – and hoped for – and was accepted by Dönitz's staff. Unfortunately, it was wildly in error. The confusion of a night battle, with torpedoes exploding in the wake and numerous depth charge explosions, combined with wishful thinking, led to exaggeration. The true figure was three escorts sunk and another damaged beyond repair.[1] The Germans, believing their own claims, saw the T5 as an excellent escort-killer.

On 15 October a pack attempted to attack ONS20 but a strong air escort kept them dived, making shadowing difficult and a concentrated attack impossible. Only one merchant ship was sunk but six U-boats were destroyed – four by aircraft, two by ships. This was the end of the wolf pack; for the rest of the war, single, submerged attack was adopted but only in small numbers. Through to May 1944 the total number of U-boats remained fairly constant at around 450, but the number at sea was halved from eighty-six to forty-three and the amount of shipping sunk per U-boat-day at sea fell to some twenty to thirty tons.

Table 7.2: Causes of U-boat sinkings, October 1943–May 1945

Cause of sinking	October–May 1944	May 1944 to the end of the war
Surface vessels	59½	85½
Aircraft	83½	163½
Submarine	3	8
Mines	3	20
Accident and unknown	13	41

Technical Developments

The withdrawal of the U-boats from the North Atlantic gave both sides the opportunity to develop new systems and technology. On the German side, there was the disastrous attempt to beat off air attack by increased gun power and the rather more successful tactic of attacking the escort vessels using homing torpedoes. Refuelling from milch cows came and went (chapter 5).[2] The RN measures were the introduction of depth-finding asdics and two successful ahead-throwing weapons. Additionally, countermeasures to

Phase 7 of the battle shows a high proportion of U-boats sunk to merchant ship losses, reflecting the balance of power that had shifted decisively to the escorting forces.

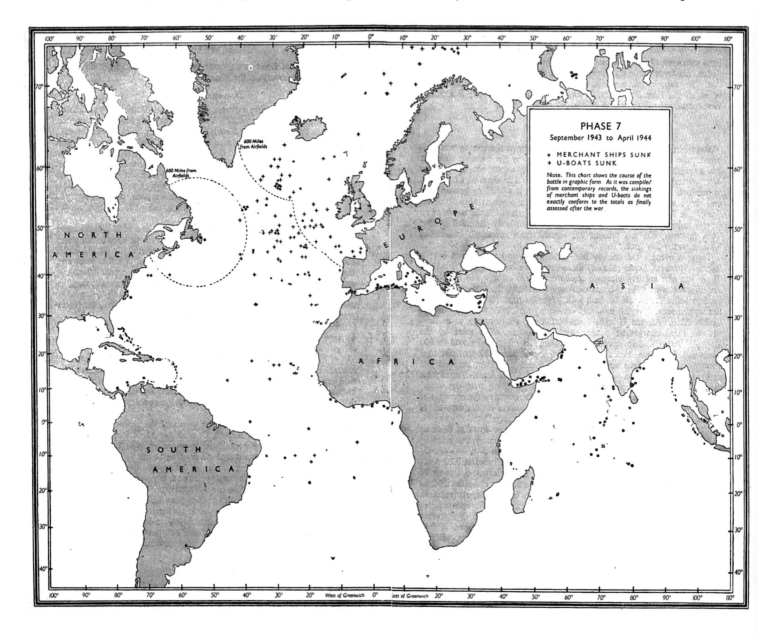

PHASE 7
September 1943 to April 1944

● MERCHANT SHIPS SUNK
+ U-BOATS SUNK

Note. This chart shows the course of the battle in graphic form. As it was compiled from contemporary records, the sinkings of merchant ships and U-boats do not exactly conform to the totals as finally assessed after the war.

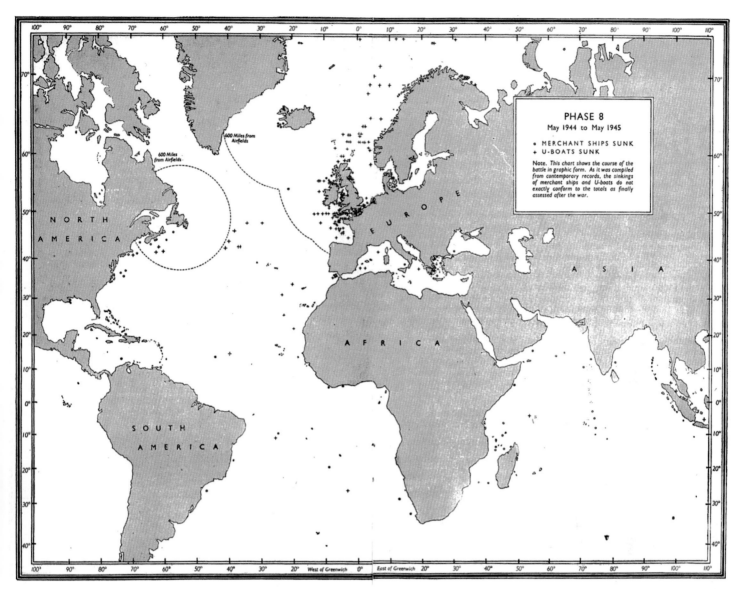

The final phase of the submarine war, after the D-Day landings in Normandy, shows a dramatic shift of theatre to the waters around the UK and the western coasts of Europe.

homing torpedoes were brought into use.

Anti-Aircraft Armament of U-Boats

From 1940, the armament of Type VII U-boats was increased by mounting a single 20mm on the bridge. This was rarely used, as most COs preferred to dive if an aircraft was sighted. By mid-1942, the armament had been increased to two twin machine guns on the bridge and a 20mm on a platform below the rear of the bridge (to be replaced by a twin when available), By June 1943, no U-boat was allowed on operations unless it had at least two 20mm. From August that year, the minimum standard was 'Conversion IV', which involved two twin 20mm on the bridge and a quadruple 20mm on the

platform below the bridge. The latter was to be replaced by a single 37mm when available from October 1943.[3]

There were a number of experimental fits. A very few boats were fitted as aircraft traps, with a very heavy armament of one 37mm and two quadruple 20mm. It is not often appreciated that additional topweight on a submarine has a twofold effect. The total weight of a submarine is fixed, equal to the weight of water displaced by the hull and appendages. This means that additional weight has to be compensated for by removal of ballast. Since the ballast is usually in the very bottom of the boat, this will cause another rise in the overall centre of gravity. Some offset was gained in April 1943, when removal of

the low-angle 88mm was permitted. These additional appendages added to the drag when submerged, with a considerable loss of speed and endurance.[4]

The standard Conversion IV fit was a powerful armament; two or more U-boats in a group formed a dangerous target and the RAF paid a heavy price for their victories. However, aircraft could form groups as well, and wait till the submarine began to submerge – a slow process with the numerous gunners to get down a single hatch. It might also be possible to call up surface ships. Once the boat had submerged, the Type 24 mine could be used (see next section).

Homing Torpedoes
Pursuit of the distinction of being 'the first' is rarely profitable, as similar developments are often taking place in several establishments at the same time and the question of who is first is a matter of chance, or of who is willing to take the biggest risk. The German T4 Falke was the first homing torpedo to be used but it was slow, at twenty knots, and only suitable for use against merchant ships. Only about 100 were made, of which some thirty were used in action from January 1943.

The American Mk 24, often referred to for security reasons as the Mk 24 'Mine' (informally as 'Fido'), was a far more effective weapon and entered service in the summer of 1943. It was dropped from aircraft and had a 92lb Torpex charge and a range of 4,000 yards at a speed of twelve knots. It is said that 346 were dropped for

Lagan was an early victim of the German homing torpedo (GNAT or T5). Few if any of the ships surviving were repaired.

Affleck, another victim, seen laid up at Barrow after the war.

68 kills and 33 damaged.[5] US aircraft dropped 142 for 31 kills and 15 damaged, the rest being by British aircraft. The first sinking appears to have been that of U-266 by an RAF Liberator of 86 squadron on 14 May 1943. It was three times as effective as an airborne depth charge. Dropped from 250 feet at 125 knots, it had a running time of ten minutes.

To maintain secrecy, very strict conditions on the use of the Mk 24 were imposed. It was not to be used near a coastline; it was not to be dropped if it could be seen by another vessel. No mention was allowed in the press, so that early post-war accounts did not mention it and, even now, the USA has not received the credit due for this very successful weapon.

The best-known homing torpedo, indeed the only one known to many people, was the German T5 Zaunkönig (code-named GNAT – German Naval Acoustic Torpedo), specifically designed to attack escorts. It had a speed of twenty-five knots on a sinuous path, which meant that ships moving at over eighteen knots were fairly safe. Ships moving at less than eight knots did not generate enough noise to attract the torpedo.

The T5 had a range of 5,700 metres. It was a very complicated device, with eleven valves and many metres of wire. Homing distance varied greatly but 450 metres for a fifteen-knot ship seems reasonable. The homing feature was inoperative for the first 400 metres of the run to protect the U-boat, and the firing pistol only sensed targets above the depth of the torpedo.

Some 640 were fired for only fifty-eight hits, much poorer than the 20 per cent success rate of other U-boat torpedoes. This was because it was often fired against difficult targets and because an effective decoy was soon introduced. The homing/firing mechanism worked well and hits were in the region of the propellers. Damage was severe; the stern was wrecked, the propellers and tail shaft were badly bent and, less obvious, the ship whipped, with buckling of the upper deck amidships in some cases. In view of the large number of escorts completing in British and US yards, few, if any, of the ships that survived a GNAT hit were repaired.

News of the German development of homing torpedoes reached the UK in the autumn of 1942 and work started on a decoy in September. 'Foxer' began to enter service soon after the introduction of the T5 but it took time to equip all escorts. Foxer consisted of a number of pipes that jangled together, making 10–100 times the noise of the ship. It was an awkward beast to handle and the noise that interfered with the GNAT also severely degraded the performance of the escort's own asdic. The life of a Foxer unit was short because of its inherent self-battering. It was gradually replaced by 'Unifoxer', a simpler device developed in Canada.

Depth-finding Asdics and Squid [6]

Some interest had been shown in depth-finding asdic in 1939 and an experimental unit was fitted in the patrol sloop *Kingfisher*, but this was damaged at Dunkirk and removed. By November 1941, work had commenced on a different device. Two sets were developed in parallel – the Q attachment for fitting to existing

sets similar to type 128, and the much more elaborate 147 for new construction.

The Q attachment had a wedge-shaped beam only 3° wide in the horizontal plane. It was mounted below the main transducer and could maintain contact with a submarine at a depth of between 300 and 700 feet at fairly close range, usually about 1,500 yards. It was tried in *Vanquisher* in February 1943. Production started in April 1943 and it entered service soon after, as ship-fitting took only two to six days. Ships with retractable domes needed docking; those with detachable domes did not.

Type 147 was a much more elaborate device. It was carried in a 'sword' ahead of the main dome. Its fan-shaped beam was 3° wide in the vertical plane and 65° in the horizontal. Ship trials took place in *Ambuscade* in May 1943. It would normally pick up the U-boat at about 800 yards and would put the correct setting on the Squid projectiles automatically.

The first operational set was installed in *Hadleigh Castle* early in September 1943. She visited the USA in December 1943, where her capability was much admired. Forty sets were supplied to the USN and 45 more by Canada.

Ahead-Throwing Weapons

After the failure of the early 'stick bomb' weapon tried in *Torrid*, there was little effort on ahead-throwing weapons until late 1939, when there was a proliferation of proposals. A study came up with two main types: a small charge (20lb) with a contact fuse and a much bigger version (200lb) with a depth-sensitive fuse, both of which would eventually enter service. Initially, there was no coordination of the various schemes and when, in late 1940, DNO was put in charge, there was a good deal of acrimony between proponents of different weapons.

The first serious proposal was the 'Fairlie mortar', in which two sets of ten mortars were fitted either side of the forecastle. The projectiles had a 20lb charge and formed a circular pattern.

Whitehall was fitted for trials with five large mortars firing standard depth charges. The mounting is seen here in A position.

The Hedgehog fired a salvo of bombs ahead of the ship. The bombs had a contact fuse so there was no 'bang' from a near miss. The charge weight was 30lb which was marginal but a change to Torpex filling was satisfactory. The drawing by John Lambert (opposite) shows a typical arrangement of a partially loaded mount.

The mortars were trained by rocking about a horizontal axis. Though this weapon did not go into service, many of its features were adopted. In January 1940, Fairlie began work, with Vickers-Armstrongs, on a three-barrelled breech-loading mortar. There was also a proposal by Thornycroft for an array of five big mortars that would fire standard depth charges. This was fitted in *Whitehall* and tested in mid-1941. It appears that the trajectory of a depth charge in the air was too variable for operational use. Lastly, there was a spigot mortar originally intended for army use but adapted by DMWD to fire contact-fused projectiles.

All these weapons needed accurate information on the position, including depth, of the submarine, which became available from the 144/147 combination. The main objection to the small charge was that it only exploded on contact and hence there was no morale effect from a near miss; but on the other hand, asdic contact was not lost in the aftermath of the explosions. A more serious objection came from DNC, who maintained that a 20lb charge was insufficient to rupture a pressure hull.[7] Goodall's diary says that the original charge was proposed at 5lb but this may have been a misunderstanding. After heated argument, the charge weight was increased to 30lb and in service even this bigger 'bang' proved marginally effective. The smaller weapon had the advantage of a smaller recoil, needing less structural support, and was therefore more suitable for small ships.

Development of the spigot mortar was actively pursued during the first half of 1940. In final form there were twenty-four charges in four rows of six. Firing was by electricity, when a spring-loaded spigot would be forced up into the base of the projectile, igniting the propellant charge. This would send the projectile on its way and at the same time compress the spring for the next round. The projectiles were fired in pairs, further minimising the recoil loading on the deck. They fell in a circular pattern about 130

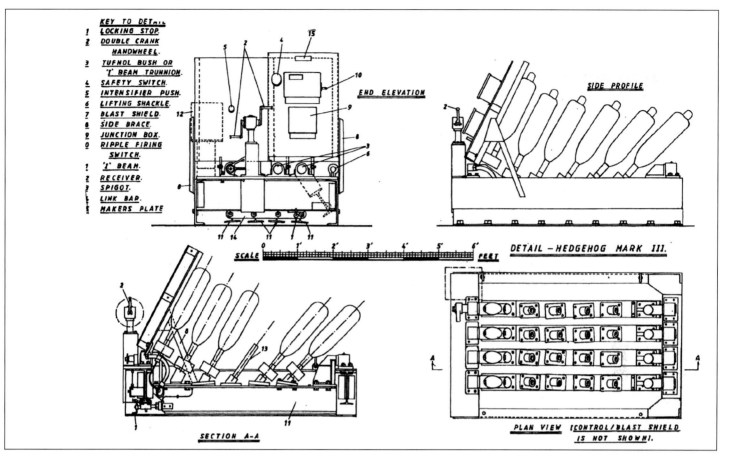

KEY TO DETAIL
1 LOCKING STOP.
2 DOUBLE CRANK
  HANDWHEEL.
3 TUFNOL BUSH OR
  'I' BEAM TRUNNION.
4 SAFETY SWITCH.
5 INTENSIFIER PUSH.
6 LIFTING SHACKLE.
7 BLAST SHIELD.
8 SIDE BRACE.
9 JUNCTION BOX.
0 RIPPLE FIRING
  SWITCH.
1 'I' BEAM.
2 RECEIVER.
3 SPIGOT.
4 LINK BAR.
5 MAKERS PLATE

END ELEVATION

SIDE PROFILE

SCALE   FEET

DETAIL – HEDGEHOG MARK III.

SECTION A-A

PLAN VIEW (CONTROL/BLAST SHIELD
IS NOT SHOWN).

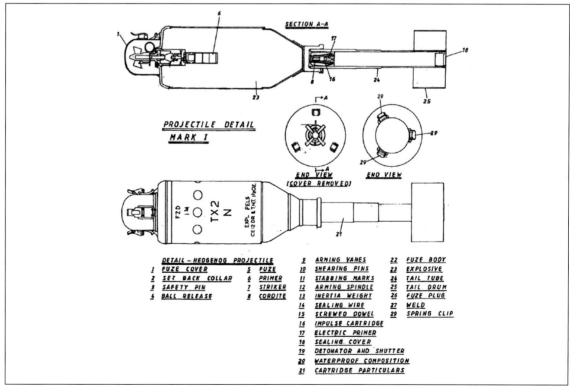

SECTION A-A

PROJECTILE DETAIL
MARK I

END VIEW
(COVER REMOVED)

END VIEW

FZD
I-4
TX2
N
EXPL. PELS
CE12 DR & TNT. 1/40Z.

DETAIL – HEDGEHOG PROJECTILE			
1 FUZE COVER	5 FUZE	9 ARMING VANES	22 FUZE BODY
2 SET BACK COLLAR	6 PRIMER	10 SHEARING PINS	23 EXPLOSIVE
3 SAFETY PIN	7 STRIKER	11 STABBING MARKS	24 TAIL TUBE
4 BALL RELEASE	8 CORDITE	12 ARMING SPINDLE	25 TAIL DRUM
		13 INERTIA WEIGHT	26 FUZE PLUG
		14 SEALING WIRE	27 WELD
		15 SCREWED DOWEL	29 SPRING CLIP
		16 IMPULSE CARTRIDGE	
		17 ELECTRIC PRIMER	
		18 SEALING COVER	
		19 DETONATOR AND SHUTTER	
		20 WATERPROOF COMPOSITION	
		21 CARTRIDGE PARTICULARS	

A post-war photo of two US Navy destroyers. The further ship has just fired a double salvo of Hedgehog and the splashes as they enter the sea may be seen ahead of her.

The single Squid fired a salvo of three projectiles each weighing 390lb with a charge of 207lb minol. The Loch class had a double mount firing a salvo of six bombs. The depth was set by asdic Type 147 at the instant of firing. It was by far the most effective A/S weapon of the war. (John Lambert)

feet in diameter.

The first tests were held in February 1941 from the pier at Weston-super-Mare (HMS *Birnbeck*), with the advantage that the projectiles could be recovered at low tide. Sea trials followed, first in *Enchantress* and later in *Westcott* (the latter ship scored one of the first kills using Hedgehog on 2 February 1942, sinking U-581). Production followed quickly.

Initial results were very disappointing. Commanding officers were reluctant to use Hedgehog because there was no bang from a near miss.[8] Hackmann tells the story of *Lotus*, which did not use Hedgehog until all her depth charges were expended and then sank her contact with the first salvo from her Hedgehog. There were mistakes in installation and a lack of maintenance information. It did not help when

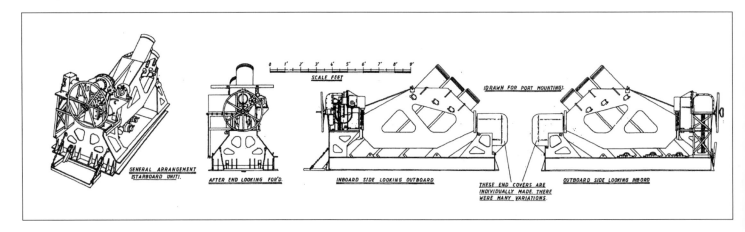

Escapade with severe damage to her bridge due to a misfiring Hedgehog. (WSS)

Escapade destroyed her own bridge with a misfiring salvo. Command even issued instructions that Hedgehog *must* be used. These problems were slowly overcome, though it was late in 1944 before the desired success rate of 20 per cent kills per salvo was achieved. The effectiveness of Hedgehog was soon increased by changing the explosive charge to Torpex, giving the equivalent of 50lb of TNT.

Hedgehog was adopted by the USN where it scored its most spectacular success. In May 1944, the uss *England* sank six Japanese submarines with twelve salvoes in eleven days.

The US developed a somewhat similar weapon for small craft, Mousetrap, firing six rocket-propelled projectiles with very little recoil.

Fears over the small size of the charge in Hedgehog projectiles led to a revival of the Fairlie mortar as 'Parsnip'. This had two rows of ten mortars, firing projectiles containing 60lb of explosive. It was tried in the ubiquitous *Ambuscade* late in 1942 but was not adopted.

Instead, the Squid was developed, also owing much to the Fairlie mortar. The single squid, used in the Castle class, was a three-barrelled mortar firing 390lb projectiles with a 207lb charge of

minol. The projectile entered the sea at a range of about 300 yards and had a sinking speed of 44ft/sec, twice that of Hedgehog, down to 900 feet. The three charges formed a triangle with 120-foot sides. A double Squid, as used in the Loch class, had two such systems set 60 feet apart in depth. The mortars could be tilted by 30° to allow for roll and yaw and small errors in course. It could be tilted to the horizontal for rapid power-loading.

Sea trials took place in May 1943 from *Ambuscade* – again – and production sets entered service in *Hadleigh Castle* in September. In general, fitting was limited to new construction but *Escapade* was fitted after the destruction of her bridge by Hedgehog. The great advantage was that the depth setting on the charges was set and updated continuously by asdic Type 147

until the moment of firing. It pleased the operators as it provided an explosion from a near miss – though with a near 50 per cent success rate from a double salvo, there were not all that many near misses. One of the early successes was that of *Loch Killin*, which in July–August 1944 sank U-333 and U-736 with only three salvoes. Early in 1945, the system was modified to fire against surfaced submarines, under radar control and using a 20-foot depth setting.

The Loch Class Frigates

The Loch class frigates and their associated weapon system were the first design to incorporate both a full understanding of the requirements of the Battle of the Atlantic and the capacity of wartime industry. The result reflected great credit on the Assistant Director, A W

The single Squid Mk IV mounting in a workshop setting. (John Lambert)

Watson, and his constructor, A E Kimberley.[9] Watson had designed the P boats of World War I.

Studies on two A/S designs began at the end of 1942 under A E Kimberley. One was basically an enlarged Flower with a single shaft and armed with a single Squid (see later section). The other was a twin-screw ship somewhat similar to the Rivers, with a twin Squid. The larger ship was preferred but, with the recognition that some smaller yards would not have slipways long enough to build the bigger ship, it was decided to build both designs. The Staff Requirements (that is, the official specification of requirements by the Naval Staff) were agreed and the design was frozen for two years from January 1943. The implications were a matter of concern; Goodall wrote,

This question brings us up hard at the onset against the difficulties attending anything like mass production of warships. The design must be fixed within the next month and by the end of the year [1942] no further changes can be accepted, though the ships will not commence to come out for many months and the last may not come out for more than two years from now.[10]

The first ship, *Loch Fada*, was laid down on 8 June 1943 and completed on 29 March 1944.

The design received Board Approval on 7 May 1943, despite efforts by the First Lord, Alexander, who wanted to replace the twin Squid

Loch Killisport entering harbour with her flags signalling her pendant number.

by another 4in gun – in an A/S ship! – Goodall was not amused.[11] Table 7.3 shows the general particulars as designed. Initial armament was a single 4-inch, a four barrel pom-pom, two twin and two single Oerlikons; radar 277 (271 in a few early ships), asdic 144/147. Later increased with more 20mm and 40mm.

Table 7.3: Loch class (as designed)
Displacement (tons): 1,435, 2,260 deep
Dimensions (feet): 307¼ x 38½ x 8¾, 13¼ deep
Shp and speed (kts): 5,500 = 20 (turbine 6,500 = 20.5)
Fuel (tons), endurance (miles) @ (kts): 730, 7,000 @ 15
Complement: 114

It was thought that at least 200 new escorts would be needed and first thoughts were for 120–45 of the twin-screw design (Lochs) and 70–80 single-screw ships (Castles). DNC's production division under Hannaford then carried out a very careful analysis of the availability of slips of the lengths required. Matching slips and building times for individual yards, they came up with a definitive programme for 133 Lochs and 69 Castles. In December 1942, orders were placed for 226 sets of machinery. In total, 1,150 sets were completed during the war, many of the later ones being diverted to transport ferries (LST Mk 3).

Table 7.4: Loch class – builders		
Builder	**Slips**	**Ships**
Hall Russell	2	10
Robb	4	16
Inglis	1	2
Blyth	4	18
Smith's Dock	6	37
C Hill	2	8

In building this new fleet, it was intended to use structural engineering works, mainly bridge builders, to the maximum extent. They were to prefabricate hull sections of up to two and a half tons in weight, limited by shipyard cranes, which would be taken by rail to shipyards to be built into the ship, which imposed dimensional limits on the sections (29ft x 8ft 6in x 8ft 6in). The transverse frames were arranged with riveted boundary angles joined to flanged plate inner sections. The boundary angles were interrupted at plate edges and longitudinals. Longitudinals were flat plates welded direct to the shell. Beams and girders were all simple sections, angles, flats or flanged plates.

The sections used welding or riveting, according to the experience of the contractor.

Loch Insh. In the author's view the Lochs were one of the all-time great designs.

Loch More in 1951, just after the author left her.

Riveting was usually employed for the assembly of sections in the shipyard. Careful inspection was necessary to ensure that sections made in different places actually fitted to make a fair ship. This worked well, 'parts for prefabricated frigates coming together beautifully'.[12]

It is interesting that contemporary documents refer to prefabrication as 'on American methods'. Few of these firms had the capability for much plate-bending, lacking bending slabs or facilities for hot smithing, particularly double curvature, so much attention was paid to simplifying the shape. The hollow forward waterlines of the Rivers were made straight and the sheer of the deckline was formed by three straight lines. The stern lines were curved in one direction only. Model tests at Haslar showed that these changes in shape made little difference to the power required. The above-water form was built with flat panels to a considerable extent.

The structural design was led by J L Adam of the British Corporation Classification Society (now merged with Lloyd's Register). He used longitudinal frames with deep transverse frames about five feet apart. Adam said in 1947[13] that the design was based on R Baker's design for the much smaller minesweeper *Seagull*, the RN's first all-welded ship.[14] It was estimated that the cost was about 50 per cent greater than that of traditional structure, though there was a considerable reduction in building time. It was a very clever design for the day.

The first ship, *Loch Fada*, was built by John Brown, with the involvement of a special drawing office set up in Glasgow under the British Corporation and directed by the Warship Production Superintendent (Scotland). They converted the traditional shipbuilders' drawings into a style that could be understood by structural engineers, quadrupling their number in the process. About half the fifty draughtsmen came from structural-engineering firms. The lines were laid off by the Henry Robb shipyard, who prepared many moulds (patterns). As table 7.5 shows, a very considerable number of firms were involved in this structural work. The table omits about fifty other headings and their subcontractors. It was found that very light items such as partition bulkheads were too easily distorted in transit and were better built by the

Photograph by the
author of *Loch Craggie*
from *Loch More*.

shipyard. There were some 100 subcontractors and about 1,360 units per ship.

Table 7.5: Loch class – firms involved in structural work	
Item	No of firms involved
Keel	8
Shell longitudinals	1
Web frames	2
Plating	5
Stringer and sheer	4
Lower deck	6
Upper deck	7

Much of the equipment was ordered through a central office under ADNC(P) C J W Hopkins, RCNC. They supplied 500 tons of steel each week, complete offices for W/T, radar and asdic, pumps, rudders, watertight doors, valves, side scuttles, anchor and cable gear and other items too numerous to list here. The number of different types of valve was kept to a minimum

and 2,000 were ordered each month.[15] Pipe services, cable trays and ventilation trunking were designed and made by specialist firms. The schedule was geared to completing twelve ships per month. Careful scheduling was needed to ensure that the right bit arrived at the right time and place.

There were thirteen shipyards involved in building the Lochs, of which five acted as specialist outfitters. Six shipyards supplied complete bridges and superstructures. Shipyards of this era were very conservative in their practices and there were delays until opposition to prefabrication was overcome: 'W Ayre doesn't want bridge builders on the job – I got depressed, it looks as though the builders' steady opposition to prefabrication is gaining ground.' (4.1.43)[16]

It was recognised from the start that these ships were far more complicated than earlier ships and that outfitting would be a problem: 'Engines and boilers now the limiting factor in frigates assuming we get labour for fitting out.'

Table 7.6: Loch class – early estimate of the rate of supply							
Year	1943				1944		
Quarter	1	2	3	4	1	2	3
Steel (,000 tons)	8	16	16	16	16	16	16
Engines			30	55	55	70	100
Equipments, ship fits		12	31	32	40	40	30

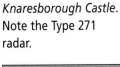

*Knaresborough Castle.
Note the Type 271
radar.*

(20.3.43) In particular, it was estimated that 400 additional electrical fitters would be needed. None of these men were found and, indeed, more were lost to the army: 'It is sticking out a mile that presently we shall have the ships ready to be fitted out but insufficient labour.' (20.4.43) Two specialised outfit centres were set up, one at Dalmuir – 'A bleak spot' (6.4.43) – for Clyde-built ships and the other at Hendon Dock for the north-east coast. Machinery installation was by NE Marine Engineering and George Clark at Hendon Dock and by John Brown at Dalmuir. At first all went well: 'Hendon Dock – work is going well. We *must* use this place more, it is well laid out and Hunter is a go-getter.' (27.1.44)

By 1945, these centres were failing to keep up with the delivery of hulls, mainly because of shortages of skilled labour, and the docks were full of incomplete hulls awaiting fitting out. By this date, the battle was almost over and delay in completion was not serious.

Altogether, twenty-eight ships were completed as Lochs, nineteen became the Bay class AA frigates, two were coastal forces depot ships, two became despatch vessels (C-in-Cs' yachts), four were converted to survey ships and fifty-four were cancelled. A few cost breakdowns are available and, although there was considerable scatter, the following is reasonably typical: hull £90,000; machinery £35,000; profit £7,000; other £3,000.

On a personal note, I first became acquainted with the capability of the Lochs whilst serving in the (unmodernised) submarine *Tabard* in a big exercise with British and US ships off Gibraltar. We had no difficulty in evading any

escort group until we met the Lochs, who had us very quickly. Soon after, I transferred to *Loch More* and learned how easy they found it to dispose of a World War II submarine. They could have coped with a Type XXI U-boat, albeit with difficulty, or a Soviet Whisky class. After an earlier spell living aft in *Chivalrous*, covered access between the fore and after parts of the ship was welcome and I swore that any ships for which I was responsible would be so designed. In my opinion the Lochs are one of the all-time great designs.

Castle Class Corvettes

The origin of the Castles has been mentioned previously, under the Loch class. The Lochs were the desired A/S ship but many smaller builders could not build ships of their length. On the other hand, the Flowers were too short for the sea-keeping needed in the North Atlantic and lacked the interior space for the later weapon and sensor systems – not to mention their crews. Smith's Dock put up a proposal for a stretched Flower and this was developed by Watson's Admiralty design team. The length was set at 252 feet overall and they were to have asdic Types 145 and 147B, controlling a single Squid with eighty-one projectiles.

After discussion with prospective builders, it was decided that they would be built by mainly traditional methods but using welding as far as yards' equipment and experience permitted. Scantlings were based on the Flowers but lightened in some areas in the search for more speed. There was a limited amount of prefabrication of structure, and wireless and radar offices were supplied complete, as were lattice masts. The design was given Board approval in May 1943.

The form was developed by tank tests at the Admiralty Experiment Works (AEW), Haslar, and though the new ships were 420 tons heavier than the Flowers and had the same engine, they were half a knot faster, largely because of the increase of 37 feet in length.

Twenty-nine were completed; all Canadian orders were cancelled in December 1943 but twelve UK-built Castles were transferred to RCN.

Table 7.7: Castle class – builders

Builders	Slips	Ships
J Lewis	3	9
J Crown	2	8
Smith's Dock		2 (prototypes)
Fleming and Ferguson	4	14
Ferguson	3	10
G Brown	3	10
Inglis	4	14

Armament was a single 4in gun and two twin and two single Oerlikons, with provision for four more Oerlikons on the quarterdeck. Type 277 radar was fitted (early ships had 272), along with HF/DF, asdic Types 145 and 147B,

Table 7.8: Castle class
Displacement (tons): 1,580 deep
Dimensions (feet): 252 x 36½ x 13½ mean
Shp and speed (kts): 16.5
Fuel (tons), endurance (miles) @ (kts): 480, 6,200 @ 15 (clean bottom)
Complement: 99

one three-barrelled squid with eighty-one projectiles, two depth charge throwers, one rail and fifteen depth charges.

The class's principal defect was their speed of sixteen and a half knots, which was barely adequate for Type VII U-boats and would have been quite inadequate for Type XXI. Rayner says that they were underpowered, and excessive windage made them very hard to handle at low speed.[17] They would not keep their bows to the sea but wallowed beam-on. Despite this, they were an effective use of available resources. Four of them served long as weather ships, a tribute to their sea-keeping, though many of the scientists who served in them would disagree. Five became rescue ships (qv).

Carisbrooke Castle.

8 Some Technical Aspects of the Battle

Before reaching any conclusions, it is desirable to consider some aspects of performance that affect operational effectiveness, such as stability, sea-worthiness and human factors.

Stability

The stability of older destroyers and, to a lesser extent, of other escort vessels became of increasing concern during the war. Radar aerials and their electronic boxes, extra AA guns, depth charges, etc. were added.[1] Paint, surprisingly heavy,[2] and 'come in handy' spares and tools added to the problem. Added weight, high up, will cause the centre of gravity of the whole ship to rise, while fact that the ship floats deeper in the water will usually cause the metacentre to fall.

The Royal Navy did not have formal stability standards before the war but each new design was judged in comparison with previous similar ships on metacentric height (GM), maximum righting lever (GZ) and the angle at which it occurred, and vanishing angle of stability. This comparative approach works well when there are frequent new designs and many ships at sea to provide feedback. Stability after damage is even more difficult and only approximate solutions were possible before the advent of computers. A common rule of thumb for British destroyers was that the ship should just float upright with the engine room and adjacent boiler room flooded. *Duncan* was a particular worry, as her longest boiler room was adjacent to the engine room. This is a very modest requirement by today's standards but seems to have been adequate, as only six

destroyers capsized out of thirty-seven sunk by a single torpedo hit, perhaps because they broke in half first (see later section on vulnerability).

Errors in safety standards are of two kinds. The first is obvious – that the standard is too low and the ship sinks in a moderate gale or after minor damage. The second kind of error is less obvious – that the standard is so high that operational capability is prejudiced or cost unreasonably increased. It is a fine balance to draw but many subjective accounts suggest that RN standards were not too high.[3] No undamaged British destroyer was lost through heavy weather, while other major navies lost nine in such conditions in the decade 1934–44 (see appendix III).[4] It will be noticed that many, perhaps most, of these incidents involved water ingress through intakes, weak doors and hatches. It is for this reason that naval architects distinguish between 'sea-keeping', the motions of a ship, and 'seaworthiness', which takes watertight integrity into account.

By July 1940, action was seen as necessary in the case of some older destroyers, which were required to fill fuel tanks with water ballast when empty. This was very unpopular, as the tanks had to be cleaned before refuelling, and was often ignored.[5] A year later, it was estimated that most destroyers had lost about 10 per cent of their initial GM as a result of topweight growth, and the Destroyer Section put a series of proposals to the DNC, Stanley Goodall. They proposed a minimum GM of 1.25 feet in the light condition and that the maximum GZ in this condition

Enchantress heeling, possibly while turning.

should not be less than 0.7 feet. These criteria were chosen to ease the work of calculation in pre-computer days. The section even put these as a pro forma, so that Goodall only had to tick the boxes! His response was interesting: he reluctantly accepted the criteria for intact stability, remarking that he preferred to take a risk on strength than on stability, but said that it was more important to carry additional armament that might prevent the ship being hit than to meet damaged-stability standards.[6] In 1943, consideration was given to lowering these standards but this proposal was rejected.

Sea-keeping and Seaworthiness

The North Atlantic is big, cold, wet, rough – sometimes very rough – corrosive and hard when it hits you. In bad weather, the fighting capability of a ship falls off rapidly, mainly because of the effect of the ship's motions on both the physical and mental abilities of the crew. Actual damage to the ship and its equipment may also occur; asdic domes were at risk, as were ships' boats, but there were more severe cases in which bridge fronts were pushed in and funnels lost. The effect of weather on U-boats, particularly attacking on the surface, and also on the ability of merchant ships to maintain the convoy course and speed is important. The weather also affected air support. The aim should be that surface escorts should retain much of their capability in any weather that permits submarines to attack, either on the surface or submerged. Weather damage accounted for the lower availability in the winter discussed in the next chapter. There are other weather-related problems, such as refuelling.

Table 8.1: Sea state, wave height and wind in the North Atlantic

Sea state	Sig. wave height (m)		Wind speed (kts)		Probability of sea state (%)	Wave period		Likely wave length (m)
	range	mean	range	mean		range	probable	
0–1	0–0.1	0.05	0–6	3	0.7	–	–	–
2	0–0.5	0.30	7–10	8.5	6.8	3.3–12.8	7.5	90
3	0.5–1.25	0.88	11–16	13.5	23.7	5–14.8	7.5	90
4	1.25–2.5	1.88	17–21	19	27.8	6.1–15.2	8.8	123
5	2.5–4	3.25	22–27	24.5	20.6	8.3–15.5	9.7	148
6	4–6	5.0	28–47	37.5	13.2	9.8–16.2	12.4	238
7	6–9	7.5	48–55	51.5	6.1	11.8–18.5	15	350
8	9–14	11.5	56–63	59.5	1.1	14.2–18.6	16.4	424
9	14	14.0	63	63	0.05	18.0–23.7	20.0	615

Note that sea state (SS) is *not* the same as Beaufort number, which measures wind speed. The wind speeds given in the table are only loosely related to wave height.

Table 8.1 shows sea states and corresponding measurements of wind and waves encountered in the North Atlantic. Note that there is no precise link between wave height and wind speed. The figures shown are fairly typical of those that might arise after the stated wind had been blowing steadily for several days over deep water. Subjective accounts seem to suggest that the winters 1940/1 and 1941/2 were unusually severe, but it could be that the authors were not then accustomed to bad weather.

Sea-keeping relates to the motions of a ship; seaworthiness considers the ability of the ship to withstand the effects of these motions. Such matters as the overall strength of the ship and, in particular, the security of doors, hatches, air intakes, etc. loom large in seaworthiness. Sea-keeping was not well understood during the war,

Photos of escorts in bad weather are rare. *Eyebright* pitching heavily in a moderate sea.

as it was not possible to carry out worthwhile calculations before probability theory and computers came into use.

The motions of a ship are usually considered as three bodily movements – along the length (surge), up and down (heave) and sideways (sway) – and three angular movements – see-saw lengthwise (pitch), perturbations about the set course (yaw) and roll (which needs no description). To complicate matters further, each of these motions has a displacement in length or degrees, a velocity and an acceleration, any or all of which may be important. Finally, the size, frequency and direction of the waves relative to the ship's course are important.

Fortunately, it is possible to ignore most of these factors without much loss of accuracy. The vertical acceleration produced by the combination of pitch and heave is the principal factor in seasickness, while roll acceleration is the main problem in most manual tasks. Damage to the ship and other problems of green seas sweeping the decks are largely governed by the relative motion of stem and wave crest, in turn largely dependent on the combination of pitch and heave magnitude. (Heave is greater in beam seas but is most important when combined with pitch in head seas.)

Seasickness is the most notorious effect of rough seas; it is no coincidence that the word 'nausea' derives from the Greek word for ship. The primary cause is vertical acceleration, combining the effects of pitch and heave. The worst case is between frequencies of 0.15 and 0.30Hz (cycles per second) and an acceleration greater than 0.9m/sec^2. Most people are sick occasionally, a few so badly that they cannot serve at sea. Other factors – smell, roll, tiredness, the nature of the last meal – may make people more susceptible to sickness, while acclimatisation much reduces the likelihood. Both pitch and heave in head seas are reduced by an increase in ship length. The benefits are not uniform; 20 per cent on the length of a 200-foot ship is far more valuable than 20 per cent on a 300-foot ship. The effects are most severe near the ends of a ship, and living and working spaces should be as near amidships as possible. In most wartime escorts, the mess decks were right forward and

the bridge was undesirably far forward.

In the early stages of the design of the post-war Castle class offshore patrol vessel (OPV), the author reviewed subjective accounts of life in World War II escort vessels.[7] Life in the Flowers (much the size and shape of the later Island class OPV) was dominated by their behaviour in rough seas. Weather was hardly mentioned with regard to the 300-foot Rivers, while the 240-foot Castles were in-between. It was concluded that the new OPV should be a bit longer than the wartime Castles. After a computer simulation confirmed and refined this historical approach, a length of seventy-five metres (250 feet) was chosen.

A later study based on the *Leander* class frigates suggested specific losses of capability for a 360-foot ship in bad weather (see table 8.2).[8] The views of several experienced COs were used. This was then read across on a simple comparison by length to give a comparison of the equivalent numbers of days' capability lost per year by various classes described in this book (see table 8.3).

Table 8.2: Effect of motions on fighting capability

Sea state	% loss of capability
0–4	0
5	10
6	30
7+	95

Table 8.3: Days' capability lost per year through bad weather

Class	Days lost per year
Flowers	28
Castles	21
Rivers, old destroyers	15
*Leander*s (for comparison)	9

This is a very crude comparison but has not been improved on. A more recent survey by the Institute of Naval Medicine showed that in a 200-foot ship some 65 per cent of the crew would be sick occasionally and 20 per cent frequently, while on a 300-foot ship these figures would reduce to 50 per cent and 15 per cent. There is some evidence that vertical acceleration,

The Canadian Modified Flower class *Owen Sound* in Sea State 5 - 6. The waves are probably 10-15ft high. As it was said, 'They would roll on wet grass'.

less than that causing sickness, will cause a deterioration in accurate decision-making.[9] The accuracy of laying and training a gun is largely determined by the vertical velocity at the mount. All this confirms that the Flowers were too short for ocean-going work but, of course, that is not what they were intended to do. The hull and machinery of a Castle cost little more than those of a Flower and they mainly used the same builders and slips.

The acceleration due to rolling produces a sideways force, making it difficult to keep one's feet when doing manual work (there is a small component due to sway but this is normally neglected). Hence the old saying, 'One hand for yourself and one for the ship.' This particularly affected the reloading of depth charge throwers, usually made even worse by seas washing over the deck, making it slippery. Rolling is a very complicated phenomenon, dependent on the course of the ship relative to the waves, the resistance of the ship's hull and bilge keels to rolling and the metacentric height. The metacentric height must be adequate to prevent capsize of the undamaged ship and, as far as possible, after severe flooding. Increase of the metacentric height above this value will lead to a rapid, jerky roll and big sideways forces. (In pre-computer days, the importance of metacentric height on rolling tended to be exaggerated.) Rolling is considered in more detail in the next section.

Slamming is one of the more unpleasant effects of motions. It occurs when the ship pitches so severely that the forefoot comes out of the sea, sometimes as far aft as the bridge, and then re-enters violently. Slamming depends on many factors, of which the most important are sea state, ship speed and the draught and section shape forward. In sea state 6 (four- to six-metre waves) a frigate shape with a draught of two metres would slam at about ten knots; increasing the draught to three metres would raise the speed for onset of slamming to fifteen knots; whilst four metres would give twenty-five knots (these figures are very approximate).

Destroyers were longer, shallower and faster, making them liable to slam frequently from sea state 5 upwards (3.25m). Their highly stressed hulls would shudder and shake, alarming to both captain and crew. Rivets would be loosened, particularly in the single-riveted seams that were used in the forecastle decks of most ships, causing leaks and adding to the misery in mess decks. Leaks might also occur in fuel tanks, giving poor combustion and leaving a trail of oil astern. Worse still would be leaks in reserve feed-water tanks. Damage to asdic domes was frequent, while pitching that was insufficient to cause damage could draw a flow of water containing air bubbles over the dome, much reducing asdic performance. In general, slamming would be rare in sloops, frigates and corvettes, as their speed in heavy weather was insufficient to cause it. This, perhaps, accounts for the surprising description of the Flowers as 'superb sea boats'.

The impact of a single slam could cause a bottom plate to crack but this was rare. More often, repeated slams would cause a plate to suffer fatigue failure. Slamming could increase the maximum stress in the main hull structure by up to 25 per cent and move the position of maximum stress further forward.

The frequency with which green seas sweep the deck is largely governed by the relative motion of the stem and approaching wave crests and by the freeboard. A rule of thumb used at the end of the war was that freeboard forward should be equal to $1.1 \times \sqrt{(\text{length in feet})}$. This figure was found by recording the freeboard of the classes that complained most about wetness and corresponds to about 100 'wettings' per hour.[10] Flare, in moderation, can help but freeboard is the dominant factor.

Green seas can cause actual structural damage to bridge front and funnels (the Towns and the S class destroyers were very vulnerable). Fittings such as boats and lockers were often washed overboard. The greatest danger was to the crew, too many of whom were swept away. In many classes there was no covered access from forward to aft. Later in the war, fleet destroyers were given bridges over the torpedo tubes, making the journey fairly safe even if still wet. Frigates had covered access to the quarterdeck. In almost all ships, the quarterdeck was low and the depth charge crews were often wet and sometimes swept overboard. (It has been suggested that the freeboard aft should be about half that forward.) A particularly bad example was that of the original Flowers, where the galley was aft and food had to be carried along the exposed deck to the short forecastle. The consequences of getting wet were made worse by the lack of proper facilities for drying clothing.

Weather did affect the capability of U-boats, though to a lesser extent. They had no radar and night surface attacks depended on visual sighting alone. In consequence, attacks were normally made down wind and sea, keeping spray off binoculars and giving the worst conditions for the escorts (until radar). In really heavy seas, depth-keeping at periscope depth became difficult.

Weather also affected the merchant ships, as they found station-keeping very difficult in bad weather and the convoy formation tended to break up. This was particularly the case on eastbound voyages, as the ships were lightly laden, often in ballast, the propeller and rudder were half out of the water and the high freeboard and light draft made staying on course very difficult.

Rolling – Flowers

The primary effect of rolling on operational capability is that it makes manual tasks much more difficult. As regards the Battle of the Atlantic, this particularly affected loading of depth charge throwers, always difficult but so much worse on a dark, wet night with the ship rolling violently. The angle through which the ship rolls is not the main problem but rather it is the jerky roll with rapid change of the angular speed (acceleration). Contrary to popular thinking, rolling is not a main cause of seasickness but it is tiring when it goes on day after day without respite, and exhaustion does make people more susceptible to sickness.

A ship is like a pendulum and has a natural period of roll. Rolling will be at its worst when the frequency with which it encounters waves is equal to its own natural period. However, small ships are rather like corks at the mercy of the sea and will be forced to roll at the frequency of encounter as shown in table 8.4. The period of encounter with waves will depend on the ship's course and speed, and heavy rolling can be avoided if the ship is free to choose; but a corvette escorting a convoy would have little choice of either course or speed.

Soon after the Flowers entered service, there were complaints about their rolling. To a consid-

How would you like to manhandle 400lb depth charges in this, even in the dark? HMCS *Swansea* in Sea State 6 with 17ft waves. Note two throwers with their loading gear and a rail.

Table 8.4: Flower class rolling – some examples[11]					
Ship	Wind force	Sea	Roll, out to out (°)	Full period (secs)	Metacentric height, GM (feet)
Heather	7–8	5	17	4.8–8.4	2.6
Salvia	4	3	16	6.6–8.4	2.4

erable extent these complaints were due to unfamiliarity with 'the way of a [small] ship in the sea' (Proverbs). Like most small ships of all navies, the Flowers had much shallower bilge keels than would now be fitted. Keels up to about eighteen inches deep could be made from a single plate welded or riveted to the shell plating, but deeper than this needed two plates arranged as a 'V', with more complicated attachment. There were also fears, largely unjustified, that bigger keels would lead to a significant loss of speed. Table 8.4 gives some examples of the rolling characteristics of particular Flower class vessels. The natural period of a Flower was 10–10¼ seconds, so it is clear that Watson's figures relate to forced rolling in the period of wave encounter. The Flowers were later fitted with deeper keels.

Rolling – the Captains[12]

The US-built Captain classes, both diesel- and turbo-electric, were strongly criticised for their rolling as soon as they entered service with the RN. The CO of HMS *Duckworth* wrote a very comprehensive report:

> They are agreeably dry in most weather and after riding out a sharp North Atlantic gale I can report that there is small risk of weather damage. In fact the ships behave like corks. Rolling – since this report is written at sea it is difficult to describe with reticence the nauseating movement of these vessels in the open sea . . . The violent 'lurching' is the principal controlling factor in efficiency. As gun platforms these ships are satisfactory only under the most favourable weather.
>
> Depth charge reloading is possible in a moderately heavy sea pounding the ship . . . Under average conditions however it must be an even bet whether the throwers lob their charges vertically upwards and on to the quarter deck or immediately alongside the propellers . . . Limitations on speed and course to windward impose a severe limitation on depth charge attacks while the Hedgehog is inaccurate in a short head swell on account of the unpredictable roll and the resultant tilt.

There were many similar remarks from other officers; there were men thrown out of their bunks, gyrocompass tripping, etc. A constructor confirming the general view blamed an excessive beam-to-draught ratio combined with a light armament, leading to a high metacentric height (GM) and rapid rolling. The GM was about 3.7 feet for the turbine ships and 3.9 feet for the diesels, compared with an average of some 2.5 feet for RN ships of similar size. The roll period of *Domett* was 7–7½ seconds with a GM of 4 feet, which gave typical roll accelerations of 0.3g. When rolling to 8–10°, she would give the occasional lurch to 20°.

In November 1943, it was proposed to increase the depth of bilge keels from eighteen inches to twenty-four inches and lengthen them by 27.5 feet aft, to cut openings in the longitudinal bulkhead between fuel tanks (this would have reduced the effective metacentric height but was not carried out) and to add many more depth charges. Added weights would need to be more than 14.5 feet from the centre line to increase the polar moment of inertia, which would help to reduce rolling. Both Western Approaches and the dockyards were concerned that this work would take a month, mostly in dock. However, it was thought that the improvement would be worth it. Model tests at AEW, Haslar confirmed the benefits and showed (as I would expect) that there was no discernible penalty on speed or endurance.

Full-scale trials were held with a modified and an unmodified ship of each class running in company in rough weather (see table 8.5). The

CO of *Goodall* reported, 'The violence of roll has been most noticeably reduced, now ship rolls comparatively slowly and from observation appears to be much steadier than a Castle class corvette.' His opposite number in *Grindall* wrote, 'The excessive rolling formerly experienced has been completely eliminated and provides a much steadier gun platform ... I was extremely pleased and consider the conversion of great benefit to both sea going and fighting efficiency.'

A rather strange aspect of this rolling saga is that there were no similar complaints from the USN about their ships. The RN vessels did not carry the torpedo tubes mounted on 01 deck in the US ships but it was calculated that these only added 0.16 seconds to the roll period and very little to the polar moment. It is just possible that the USN crews had less seagoing experience in other ships than their RN counterparts and thought that all ships rolled like that. This and

Grindall, a diesel-engined Captain in a moderate sea in April 1944. On first entrance into British service the class were criticised for heavy rolling.

Table 8.5: Comparisons in rough-weather performance of Captain class frigates

Class and ship	Bilge keel	Period (sec)	Roll, out to out (°)
Diesel, *Kempthorne*	Mod	8	40
Diesel, *Cooke*	Original	7½	56
Steam, *Bentley*	Mod	8½	22
Steam, *Dakins*	Original	8	48

other historical material was used by K Monk in setting and achieving a roll criterion.[13]

The sloops of the *Black Swan* class had active fin stabilisers following trials in *Bittern*. The idea was to improve the accuracy of AA gunfire but knowledge of control theory was not great during the war and they were of only limited value. Many people thought the space would be better used to carry more fuel.

Human Factors

Life on small ships in the North Atlantic was inevitably exhausting, particularly in winter. Today, it is recognised that the combat efficiency of the crew is enhanced if they are well fed and can rest properly when off duty, but this was not understood before and during the war and British ships fell well short of what was possible and desirable. There was an impression that sailors were tough and almost revelled in discomfort. In particular, it was thought that discomfort was necessary to keep men awake when on duty. During the 1930s, with high unemployment, it was easy to recruit and there was no great pressure to improve matters.

It was often claimed that hammocks were more comfortable than bunks in rough weather – though most temporary officers had started as ratings but showed no inclination to retain hammocks when promoted. The food supplied was adequate both in quality and quantity but the way it was prepared, cooked and served was primitive and unlikely to provide a balanced diet.

Ventilation in most ships was grossly inadequate, contributing to the high incidence of tuberculosis, and the first fifty-six British-built Flowers completed without lining on their sides. From 1940 the sides were sprayed with asbestos fibres, which would lead to the deaths of many dockyard workers in years to come. Washing and toilet facilities were crude and in inadequate numbers.

The early, short-forecastle Flowers were the worst. They had bunks right forward, where the motion was the most violent. To reach the bridge or engine room, it was necessary to cross the open well deck, getting soaked if the weather was rough. Worse still, the galley was aft and food had to be brought along the open upper deck, getting cold or spilt on the way. As more equipment was added, overcrowding got worse. The following quotation from a Canadian sailor sums it very well:

It was sheer unmitigated hell. She was a short fo'c'sle corvette and even getting hot food from the galley to the fo'c'sle was a tremendous job. The mess decks were usually a shambles and the wear and tear on bodies and tempers was something I shall never forget. But we were young and tough and, in a sense, we gloried in our misery and made light of it all. What possible connection it had with defeating Hitler none of us bothered to ask. It was enough to find ourselves more or less afloat the next day and the hope of duff for pudding and a boiler clean when we reached port.[14]

Life in the raw! Preparing the joint of meat mixed with depth charges on a corvette. (IWM A6358)

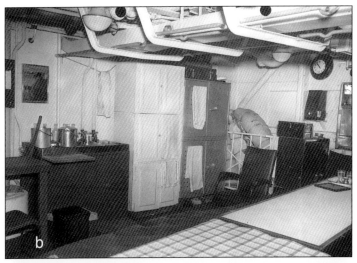
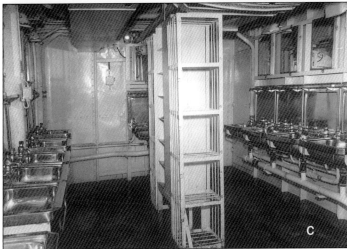

A sequence of interior views of *Loch Ruthven*. These clean and empty pictures fail to show the horrors of a mess deck full of wet and dirty sailors.

a. PO's mess.
b. Another view
c. Crew's washplace
d. Stoker's mess
e. Open Bridge *(over page)*

The frigates were a little better, as they were longer, reducing vertical motions. They had covered access fore and aft, and their later design remedied some of the detail faults of the Flowers. But with only a little thought and a slight increase in cost, much of this discomfort could have been avoided (see Monsarrat's comparison of the River and Colony equipment in chapter 6).

Some of these problems arose, as discussed above, from the belief that sailors should be tough. There was little experience of sustained bad weather, as peacetime exercises were usually held in times and areas where bad weather was unlikely and peacetime budgets did not allow for ships to be driven at speeds where damage was liable to occur. It was well known to naval architects and naval officers that motion was worse at the ends of the ship, yet mess decks were right forward – and the captain and admiral had the other end! Much of this problem was due to a failure to quantify the magnitude of the motion. The author as a student was taught that motion was worst at the ends but not given any real idea of how much worse. A full study of motions needed a computer and knowledge of probability theory, but much could have been done by taking measurements along the length of several ships in bad weather.

Another recurring problem was leakage through upper-deck riveted seams, usually single-riveted. To come off watch soaking wet and find that your mess deck, including your locker with change of clothes, was also soaking was good for neither morale nor health. Exercises usually avoided the season of bad weather and were very often in fairly southerly latitudes, convenient for

both Home and Mediterranean Fleets. It has long been the author's contention that one squadron of ships of different classes should proceed at all times at the highest possible speed with the intention of seeing what breaks or is incapacitated.

There were sporadic attempts to set up welfare committees but these were mainly concerned with detail and foundered on lack of funds. It is strange that the two best books dealing with living are both described as 'fiction'.[15]

Bridge design was an emotional subject, but RN opinion was unanimous in advocating open bridges. With 30–50 per cent of first contacts being by eyeball up to the end of 1942, it seems that they were right. Nevertheless, there was an unrecognised price to pay, primarily in exhaustion, leading to impaired decision-making. The USN tended to favour enclosed bridges and gun houses.

Escape

Losses of escorts during the battle were not unduly severe but, even so, some of their crews found sleeping difficult in the lower mess decks and cabins, with a long and tortuous route to the upper deck, and preferred to rest, if possible, closer to the deck. Most of those ships torpedoed sank in under ten minutes. Adequate escape routes add greatly to peace of mind when sinking may be rapid, and men will stay at their posts longer when they know they can get out quickly.

Very little consideration had been given to

lifesaving gear before the war (see chapter 3). Boats could not be lowered in time and neither they nor Carley floats gave any protection from exposure. Just before the war, the inflatable lifebelt was shown to be dangerous in tests but was put into production without change. A very high proportion of those who escaped from sinking ships died of exposure in the water.[16] Picking up exhausted survivors from the water was an all-too-frequent task and one to which little thought had been given.

Vulnerability

Escort vessels of the Battle of the Atlantic were relatively small ships and unlikely to survive a torpedo hit. Of 140 destroyers and other escorts hit by a torpedo, worldwide, 102 sank. It is not easy to be specific concerning the number of escorts sunk during the battle, as, in addition to the usual difficulty of defining the area, some were on passage. However, the figures shown in table 8.6 are of the right order.

Table 8.6: Losses of escort vessels in the Atlantic[17]

Type	RN	Allied
Destroyer	15	13
Sloop	9	–
Frigate	4	7
Corvette	7	4

Table 8.7 shows a summary of the time taken for various types of warship to sink. It is not often realised that back-breaking was the principal cause of sinking for the smaller ships of World War II. Broken backs accounted for 44 per cent of destroyer losses, 40 per cent of frigates and 21 per cent of sloops. It may be assumed that the great majority of those that sank quickly broke their backs. The destroyer was highly stressed overall, but the break of forecastle close to amidships exacerbated the problem, making it most likely to fracture. The long forecastle and lower stresses of the sloop and frigate increased survival time.

It is interesting that fire was not a serious problem: of 496 destroyers hit by any weapon, only sixty reported fire, mostly due to bombs, which were not a feature of the Atlantic battle. Caution is needed in assigning a single cause of loss; a ship may be blazing furiously, on the point of capsize when it breaks in half.

Speed

Speed was a valuable asset in an A/S vessel. There were several criteria, the first being that the vessel should have a substantial speed margin over a surfaced submarine, say seventeen-plus knots. The speed of a submerged submarine did not normally exceed three to four knots, although nine knots could be reached for a short period. In hunting submerged targets, the limit was set by asdic performance, constraining speed to about fifteen knots.

The most important aspect of speed lay in rejoining a convoy after falling astern during a prolonged hunt. Convoy speed was seven to nine knots in good conditions and contemporary views were that a speed of about twenty-five knots was needed to catch up after a hunt lasting some hours. Only the destroyers (including long-range conversions) and the steam-powered Captain class were that fast. Given an adequate number of escorts, the senior officer would always detach a fast ship for prosecuting a contact. The success of destroyers and the steam-powered Captain class in terms of kills is largely due to their more frequent opportunities. The comparison between steam and diesel Captains is notable. The use of high speed was expensive in

Table 8.7: Time to sink after damage in action (worldwide figures)

Type	Time to sink (minutes)				
	less than 10	10–19	20–29	30–59	60+
Destroyer	28	12	1	1	2
Sloop	2	1	1	3	3
Frigate	3	-	-	1	4
Corvette	13	2	1	2	5

terms of fuel consumption and fast ships needed more fuel (see next section).

The Flowers failed by all of these criteria but high speed was not essential for every member of an escort group. The corvettes' role was that of a mobile asdic set, locating submerged attackers and deterring surface attack. It is interesting to note that the bigger Castle class, with the same engine as the Flowers, were at least half a knot faster as a result of their improved hull form, developed at AEW, Haslar.

Endurance

'O Lord be kind, thy sea is so big and my ship is so small.' (FISHERMAN'S PRAYER)

The Atlantic is big: from New York to Liverpool is 3,043 nautical miles; Halifax to Liverpool, 2,485 nautical miles; and Panama to Liverpool, 4,530 nautical miles. The typical convoy route was some 3,000 miles long, requiring fourteen to nineteen days to traverse along a route very close to a great circle. Most maps (including those used in this book) are Mercator's projection, which greatly exaggerates the scale at higher latitudes, making convoy routes appear far from direct. Escorts would travel considerably further, zigzagging and searching for contacts, and they would also use higher speeds from time to time. Table 8.8 shows the effect of speed on endurance for a V&W class destroyer.

Wanderer in an early trial of replenishment at sea.

Table 8.8: Effect of speed on endurance (V&W destroyer)	
Speed (kts)	Endurance (miles)
15	3,500
18	1,800
32	900

Refuelling at sea only came into use in 1942 and was a slow and unreliable process, possible only in good weather. The older destroyers could not cross the Atlantic without refuelling and some other classes had only a marginal capability. The long-range escorts (mainly V&W conversions) lost a boiler room, and with it a few knots in speed, to gain a bigger fuel stowage. In many classes, the need to conserve fuel limited the use of high speed.

Table 8.9 shows the endurance of various classes of escort. These figures have been drawn from different sources and are not entirely consistent. In any case they are nominal figures and the actual endurance at sea was much less. Note the gradual improvement in pre-war destroyers. Note also the economy of the diesel Captains.

Turning Circle

A small turning circle was needed to position the stern for a successful depth charge attack on a submerged U-boat. It was also desirable to be able to turn inside a U-boat that was fighting it out on the surface. The Flowers were outstanding in this respect – short and with a fair-sized rudder in the slipstream of the propeller. The British twin-screw ships were less good and it is hard with hindsight to see why there was so much reluctance to use twin rudders in the Rivers and Lochs. Table 8.10 gives some typical figures; note how the diameter varies with speed.

Table 8.10: Turning circle		
Class	Diameter (yards)	Speed (kts)
Flower	136	
River, Loch	330–400	12
Captain DE	280	16
Captain TE	350	18
RN Destroyer	370	10
	405	15
	600	30
Town	770	15

Table 8.9: Endurance of various classes of escort				
Class	Miles @ kts	Fuel (tons)	Long-range versions Miles @ kts	Fuel (tons)
Destroyers				
B	2,440 @ 14	390		
E	3,550 @ 14	480		
H	4,000 @ 14	329		
V&W	2,180 @ 14	367	2,680 @ 14	450
Town	2,000 @ 14	284	2,780 @ 14	
Sloops				
Fowey	4,000 @ 14	329		
Black Swan	4,710 @ 14	425		
Frigates and corvettes				
Flower	3,850 @ 12	233	(5,650 with WT boilers)	
Castle	7,800 @ 12	480		
River (triple expansion)	4,630 @ 14	470	6,600	
River (turbine)	4,920 @ 14	470	7,000	
Loch	4,670 @ 14	730		
Captain DE	4,670 @ 14	197		
Captain TE	3,870 @ 14	335		

9 Production:
Building Ships to Win the Battle

The British shipbuilding industry suffered badly during the series of depressions in the twenties and thirties, with the closure of about thirty shipyards. The smaller yards suffered most; Beardmore and Palmer were the only major yards to close completely. A drip-feed of orders had kept the thirteen specialist warship builders in business. With the start of rearmament, these specialists had become overloaded and it was clear that escorts would have to be built by yards unaccustomed to warship-building. The marine engineering industry had suffered even more badly and the capacity for key items such as reduction gearing, turbine blades and water-tube boilers was much smaller than in 1918. The Vickers-Armstrongs group was the only firm capable of producing major weapons, while armour production was of serious concern. Modern machine tools were scarce, as was welding equipment.

These cuts in the shipbuilding area had a number of knock-on effects. Perhaps the most serious was on recruitment. Shipbuilding was no longer the sort of job that attracted bright young men either at tradesman level or as graduates. This led to a very old-fashioned approach to new technology. There was a belief that the collapse of Beardmore was due to over-investment in new equipment followed by inability to keep up interest payments on the loans needed to finance this work. In consequence, there had been very little investment in any new equipment. The frontispiece of Buxton's *Big Gun Monitors* shows the main slipway and fitting-out basin of John Brown's yard in 1916 and 1941. The only change is the addition of a single tower crane in the later view.

Unions, concerned to protect the remaining jobs for their members, rigidly enforced many restrictive practices such as demarcation and tended to oppose new technology, particularly if it was intended to save labour. These practices led to strikes, further reducing any profits that might have fed back into investment in capital equipment. However, not all was doom and gloom; there were still sixty shipyards with double the output of their nearest overseas competitors and output per man was high.

Following the outbreak of war, the demand was overwhelmingly for numbers and, as explained in chapter 2, the only design that could be produced in numbers by non-specialist ship- and engine-builders was the Flower class; ninety ships were on order in the UK by September 1939, and a further sixty-four in Canada. The thirteen regular warship builders were fully occupied with major warships and were only able to contribute a few *Black Swan*s and the prototype Loch. Swan Hunter built a few Castles and Lochs. There was a remarkable variation in the building times, both from ship to ship in the same yard and from yard to yard.

Table 9.1: Flower class building times (UK-built ships)	
Statistics type	**Build time, laying down to completion (months)**
Quickest individual ship	5.0
Slowest	22.0
Best average (Smith's Dock)	6.5
Worst average (Ailsa)	19.0

Loch Fada was built in conventional style by John Brown. Drawings were taken off so that engineering companies unused to shipbuilding could pre-fabricate sections for later ships.

Variation within a yard was sometimes due to bombing, which would also account for some of the variation between yards, while late delivery of equipment was a continuing problem It is interesting that later ships usually took longer than earlier ones, contrary to the expected benefits of the 'learning curve'. The longer time reflects the combined effects of bombing, shortages of both labour and materials and of war-weariness. It has been suggested that malnutrition during the depression may have contributed. The more extensive electronic equipment in later ships was also a factor.

As described above, management, labour relations, trade union practices and capital equipment were all outdated, while the blackout and air raid alarms created further difficulties. At one meeting, a prominent shipbuilder, Sir James

Lithgow (then Controller of Merchant Shipbuilding), said that shipbuilding practices were out of date. Stanley Goodall wryly noted in his diary, 'Satan rebuking Sin.'[1] Despite all these problems, Buxton has shown that the remarkable building times achieved in the USA were at the cost of much greater man-hours per ship and possible only because of the vast resources of manpower and material available.[2]

A crude comparison of building times for various classes of escorts shows British yards in a bad light (see table 9.2). In particular, US dates are for commissioning, usually a few weeks before completion. These figures tell only part of the story, and that the unfavourable part. Man-hour figures are scarce but early US DEs required about one million man-hours, reducing to 600,000 with experience. In contrast, British-built Rivers needed 350,000–400,000 man-hours for a somewhat simpler ship.[3] It is also noteworthy that US-built Liberty ships cost $1.78 million (equivalent then to £450,000), while a similar British-built Empire cost about £180,000.

Strikes were a serious problem, with about one million working days lost in 1944, over three times the 1939 figure. There seems to have been an idea that the war was being fought to preserve British liberties, including the right to strike in defence of trade union practices. There was probably some communist agitation prior to the German attack on the Soviet Union. Between 1938 and 1945, average wages in engineering roughly doubled from £3.50 to £7 per week. This did not go down well with the naval crews of vessels fitting out. A petty officer's pay had gone up from £2.50 to £3.50 per week, with much longer hours (and no overtime pay), discomfort and considerable danger.

Official figures in thousands for employment in shipbuilding and repair for naval work are shown in table 9.3. Similar figures for marine engineering show 58,000 before the war, 88,900 in June 1943 and 80,500 in June 1945. Many engines were diverted from Lochs and Castles to the landing ship programme. The problem lay more in the balance between trades than in overall numbers. For example, the number of welders on naval work increased 80 per cent during the war. There was considerable pressure from the DNC department for ever more welding, which was lighter and stronger (at least if properly carried out). However, welding required new equipment that was not readily available in wartime Britain and, since few yards had the space or facilities for welded construc-

Table 9.2: Comparative building times (months/days)

Class	Country of build	Fastest (months/days)	Slowest (months/days)
River	British	7/5	24/17
River	Canadian	5/3	17/6
River	Australian	16/8	24/15
Colony	US	5/0	21/8
Loch	British	7/25	17/10
Evarts	US	3/3	21/20
Buckley	US	1/23	13/21
Flower	British	4/3	20/3
Flower	Canadian	7/26	17/24
Castle	British	5/12	17/24

Table 9.3: Employment in naval shipbuilding and repair (000s)

Work item	June 1940	September 1943	June 1945
Naval, new build	62.4	89.3	73.9
Repair and conversion	41.5	44.1	38.8
Dockyards	26.4	36.7	73.9
Total, naval	130.3	170.1	148.4
Grand total	203.1	272.5	252.3

Table 9.4: Costs and installed electrical power

Class	Cost (£000)	Cost per ton (£)	Installed electrical power (kW)	Displacement (tons)
Flower	90	95	15 (later doubled)	900
Castle	190	175	105	1,060
River	240	175	180	1,370
Loch	300	209	180	1,435
Black Swan	360	217	190–360	1,470

tion, in the short term it made sense to use the skilled riveters already available.

The shortage of electrical fitters got worse, as discussed under the Loch class programme. Installed electrical power is an indication of the complexity of the ship and, as table 9.4 indicates, is reflected in the overall cost. Degaussing, radar, heating and ventilation all made demands on electrical power generation and cabling.

There can be a considerable difference between the price paid to the shipbuilder (and engine manufacturer) and the total cost to the Admiralty, as many items of equipment were ordered centrally in bulk and supplied to the yard – even machinery in the later years. For a destroyer, the shipyard cost was about 80 per cent of the total. Ships were still ordered in accordance with an approved annual programme but changing priorities and availability of slips and of equipment caused many variations.

Some 27,000 women were recruited and though few were employed on production, they released men for heavier duties.

Production in the USA

Production in the USA had some, but not all, of the UK problems and these were less severe. There were no air raids – not even blackout – and labour was plentiful. There was an overriding intent that escort production should not interfere with the production of major warships down to, and including, destroyers. This meant using shipyards unaccustomed to warship work, and even many new yards on 'green-field' sites. In turn, this obliged the US Navy (including the US Maritime Commission) to fund a significant amount of capital equipment, even in the existing yards. There were severe bottlenecks in the supply of major components such as engines, gearboxes and 5in guns, etc. The results were outstanding.[4]

The first order came in November 1941 for fifty escorts for the RN under Lend-Lease. America's entry into the war meant that the RN received only six of the original fifty, but this was more than compensated for by the eventual delivery of thirty-two diesel-electric (GMT) and forty-six turbo-electric ships (TE). Within a year, 1,005 DEs were on order, of which 563 from six

different classes were completed (including fifty-six fast transports). The first were laid down in February 1942.

Initially, there was delay in starting as landing craft were given priority, but production built up rapidly from mid-1942. RN ships came mainly from Boston Navy Yard (GMT) and Bethlehem-Hingham (TE), though there were exceptions. Most RN Captains completed in the second half of 1943. There is a story that at Bethlehem-Hingham (which cost the US Navy $35 million), each ship taking shape on the long line of sixteen slipways was one week behind its neighbour and would be launched when its turn came, regardless of any outstanding work. At peak this yard employed 23,000 workers. There were a total of seventeen yards involved in the whole DE construction programme, of which the six biggest accounted for 73 per cent of the ships built. The new yard at Orange, Texas built ninety-three DEs, using 20,000 workers. Despite the slow start, the DE production output was invaluable, in the Pacific as well as the Atlantic.

Just in case 1,000 DEs were not enough, in June 1942 the US Maritime Commission suggested that there was some spare capacity in small merchant shipyards, including some on the Great Lakes. The Canadian-built River class was selected as a prototype (PF), with the structure modified by Gibbs and Cox for welded, prefabricated construction – and habitability to USN standards. Altogether, 100 were ordered, of which twenty-one joined the RN, all built by Walsh-Kaiser (Providence, RI). That yard averaged two and a half months from laying down to launch, with a further five months to completion. The ships were commissioned from the very end of 1943, with most joining in early 1944. As discussed in chapter 6, most had machinery teething problems, which delayed acceptance considerably.

US sources suggest that there was a structural weakness in the class. Since the Rivers had no such difficulties, it must be assumed that the PF problems were due to weld details.

The Canadian Contribution

Before the war, the RCN had only thirteen ships, mostly built in the UK, which grew to about 375

by the end of the war. The Canadian shipbuilding and supporting industries were tiny but they expanded very rapidly. For the Battle of the Atlantic, they built 60 Rivers for the RCN, with 2 for the USN and 8 for the RN. Then there were 97 RCN Flowers, 17 for the RN and 8 for the USN. This was not all, as Canadian yards built 4 Tribal class destroyers, 122 ocean minesweepers, 16 trawlers, 172 MLs, MTBs, etc., 26 Landing Ships Tank and 18 maintenance ships, not to mention a large number of Fort class merchant ships – a wonderful achievement.[5] Numerous problems arose, mainly due to inexperienced staff, but these were all overcome thanks to the willingness and enthusiasm shown by all concerned. Pre-war experience in Canada was largely with machine work and it was difficult to develop the hand-working skills needed for ships' machinery.

Initially, it was intended that Canada would

An aerial view of the Bethlehem-Hingham shipyard. The sixteen slipways built turbo-electric Captains for the RN.

build hulls and main machinery but rely on the UK for auxiliaries and armament. The first fourteen Flowers 'completed' without guns, and at least two crossed the Atlantic with wooden dummies. The earliest ships required some reworking in the UK. After the fall of France, this became increasingly difficult and more and more items were home-grown. It was an all-Canadian effort, though valuable guidance was given by the British technical team headed by the constructors Stanton and, later, Harrison. Canada even produced her own radar (SW-1 and SW-2), which was no worse than the contemporary RN Type 268. Overseeing was in the hands of local staff of the Classification Societies, Lloyd's and British Corporation. These were not accustomed to Admiralty Standards and had to be convinced. Trials were a particular problem, as they could not see the need for lengthy and detailed records. In the UK, the specialist naval schools – gunnery, torpedo, etc. – played an important part in setting systems to work. The tiny RCN lacked comparable schools but played an increasing role as experience developed.

Canada had her own specific problems, such as the size of the country; it is 3,500 miles from Halifax to Victoria. Imagine the waste of time if an officer had to travel this distance by train. Moreover, winter temperatures caused many difficulties, including ice blocking the Saint Lawrence. Uncompleted ships were often towed downriver as winter approached. There was little experience in Canada of working from outline drawings, with each shipyard producing its own working drawings. Drawing offices were small, even non-existent, and their staff lacked the education and experience of UK draughtsmen. Detailed drawings had to be produced in the UK, which meant that at least one ship of the class had to have been built, delaying the start of the Canadian programme. Some of the drawings supplied were not fully corrected up to date. Once complete, the drawings had to come by sea, as there was no regular airmail until 1941. The locks on the canal from the Great Lakes to the Saint Lawrence were only 270 feet long, so that frigates could not be built on the lakes.

Main engines were built by five firms. Initially, one was not satisfactory – it was found that only one man in the company had worked on marine engines before – but they learned quickly. Details could cause serious problems. In the early days there were problems with brittle bolts, due, it was found, to the use of steel with high sulphur and phosphorus content. Everything was rushed and much of the steel used in the hulls was still covered in mill scale. Normally, plates and sections would have been stored in the open for some time and the scale would have fallen off, but in war there was no time and ships completed still covered in scale. This would be painted over, and both scale and paint would fall off at sea, giving the scruffy look wrongly attributed by the RN to ill discipline.

It was hoped that many auxiliaries would come from the UK but they were in short supply there, too, and some were lost in transit. Valves were a particular problem. Gyrocompasses were unobtainable and most Canadian Flowers had to rely on a single magnetic compass (without repeaters) until late in the war. This caused navigational problems, particularly after exposure to shock, but worse, the gyrocompass formed part of the asdic control system and the magnetic unit was less reliable. Eventually the problems were overcome and Canada became self-supporting.

Canada was even less well positioned to carry out refits. For various reasons it was mid-1942 before it was decided to update the Canadian Flowers and work did not commence till the beginning of 1943. The work involved lengthening the forecastle, a new bridge, Hedgehog and associated Type 144 asdic. The latter involved big changes to the electrical supply and distribution systems. The package took about twenty-two weeks in Canada, compared with fifteen weeks in the UK and ten in the USA.

All these ships had to be manned with trained crews, a problem discussed in chapter 3. Initially, Canadian ships went to sea built by inexperienced yards, lacking important equipments and with inexperienced crews. It is no wonder that there were problems at first but, more notable is the speed with which such problems were overcome to make Canada's contribution to victory.

Australian ships played no significant part in

Over page: The Canadian River class *Swansea* in heavy seas. It is probably Sea State 7 with waves up to 25ft high (estimating wave heights from photos is not easy). She seems to be riding them well.

the Battle of the Atlantic but, starting in 1939, the RAN promised to supply twelve A/S officers and twelve SD (special duties) ratings every two months, and numbers subsequently increased.[6]

Availability

For various reasons, a considerable number of escort vessels were not available at any given time. There were material problems, such as boiler cleaning, general maintenance, repairs, etc., and the crew needed rest and, if possible, leave. More and more time was devoted to training, both individually and for the complete group. Table 9.5 shows the results of a post-war analysis of the non-availability of escorts. The impact of damage during the evacuations of 1940 is apparent, while one may also note the effect of weather damage in the winter months. The early Flowers often completed with poorly aligned crankshafts, leading to early bearing failure. The older British destroyers had no intrinsic problems but old age led to continual difficulties with leaking rivets, making life unpleasant for the crew and causing contamination in both fuel and feed-water. The Towns suffered from incurable 'condenseritis' as the tube plates were weak and not parallel, from bearing problems due to corrosion of the cast-iron housings and from leaky rivets and a bridge structure too weak to withstand the impact of heavy seas.

Neither the diesel nor the turbine Captains had any serious maintenance problems, showing that a complex system is not necessarily unreliable. As discussed, the Colony class had initial machinery problems but seem to have given few troubles in service.

Table 9.5: Percentage of escorts unavailable for operations		
Year	Winter/spring (%)	Summer/autumn (%)
1939	17.0 (autumn/winter)	
1940	20.7	25.0
1941	8.3	19.0
1942	19.3	18.8
1943	24.0	19.0
1944	24.8	18.6
1945	24.6	
Whole war	23.3	19.3
Note: The overall average was 22.0 per cent		

10 Evaluation: How Good Were They?

It is of little value to search for the 'best' A/S vessel. This leads directly to a paradox described by the Soviet naval architect Khudyakov, with at one extreme the super-battleship, the finest fighting ship of all time, but so expensive that no navy can afford more than one, and at the other the Chinese junk, cheap enough to build in numbers but having little or no operational capability.

The overall objective of the RN and its allies was the safe arrival of merchant ships and their cargoes, and the best A/S vessel was the one that used available resources most effectively to that end. Both capability, in terms of sensors and weapons, and resources change over time and led to different choices. The following paragraphs will review the decisions made at different times, both in the light of information then available and with hindsight.

Before the War

In the early 1930s there was no perceived threat in the Atlantic. The only significant submarine forces were those of the USA and France, and war with either was inconceivable. In the Pacific, Japan was increasingly hostile but it was believed (rightly) that their submarine doctrine was focused on attacking the US battlefleet.

The 1932 review of A/S capability assumed an enemy submarine force based in the North Sea. This 'enemy' was not named but was presumably Germany, even though that country had no submarines at that date. It was considered that few submarines would be operational in the Atlantic, because of the long passage time round the north of Scotland, and

these few could be dealt with by the older destroyers and sloops. This view appears to show an underestimate of the endurance of the Type VII. Much preliminary work was put in hand for the introduction of convoys. One may also wonder how effective the sizeable U-boat fleet of 1942–3 would have been if it had been based solely in Germany. The rate at which U-boats could be built was also underestimated.

There was also an awareness of the need for faster escorts; twenty-five knots was suggested but such ships lay outside the twenty-knot limit for minor warships set by the London Treaty. Higher speed meant turbine machinery and, probably, a lighter warship structure, all making them costly and reducing the size of the manufacturing base. Recommendations for heavier armament were implemented in later sloops, as was the separation of the A/S sloop from the minesweeper role. Sensible proposals for east-coast escorts led to prototypes of both a converted commercial trawler and an Admiralty design consistent with trawler building methods. Some destroyers of the V&W classes were converted into AA ships.

It was recognised that trawlers were on the small and slow side even for coastal work and early in 1939 another review led to the Flower class corvette. As shown in chapter 2, the choice of the Flower was almost inevitable in terms of numbers needed, building slips, machinery fit, etc. Similarly, there was no choice in weapon system; the 120-series asdic and depth charge was the only system available. A design similar to the Castle but with depth charges would have been more capable and little more demanding on resources. Franklin has shown that Roskill was wrong in saying that there were no A/S convoy defence exercises between the wars,[1] but there were not many[2] and the lessons learnt do not seem to have reached the top.

The Admiralty faced numerous, severe threats worldwide and, not unnaturally in the lack of a perceived submarine threat, concentrated on the bigger ships that took so long to build. Battleships, aircraft carriers, cruisers and destroyers, with a very few sloops, filled every slipway in the remaining warship yards to such an extent that programmes were delayed and the sums voted by Parliament could not be spent.[3] More money would not have been sufficient in itself.

The heavy workload in traditional warship yards meant that any increased number of escorts would have to be built in yards unaccustomed to warship work. Many of these yards were small and the length of their building slips limited escorts to about 240 feet. The effect of length on sea-keeping is non linear: a 240-feet ship is much better than a 200-feet one but the benefit of further increases to 280–300 feet is less. Thus the Castles had much better sea-keeping than the Flowers but were only slightly inferior to the even-longer Rivers.

Machinery production was a greater problem. Machine tools of all kinds were scarce and those that were available were often old-fashioned. Turbine blade production was limited and reduction gearing even more so. The only readily available engines were the triple-expansion, four-cylinder units based on that designed by Smith's Dock for the *Southern Pride* and, though these could be built by many yards, their production still set a ceiling on numbers. This limit favoured the single-screw ships such as Flowers and Castles. Geared turbines were used in sloops and a few Rivers and Lochs. Diesels were thought unreliable at continuous power and there was little manufacturing capacity. It was also thought, probably incorrectly, that wartime crews would not be able to handle more advanced machinery. However, they had no problems with the machinery in either type of the Captain class, with only a brief conversion course. It was also thought that the simple plant would be reliable and easy to maintain. Experience with the Captains showed this idea, too, to be wrong.

Anti-submarine systems progressed quite well, considering the low priority given to ASW and the general shortage of funds. The UK electronics industry was somewhat backward. However, the RN had the best sensor in the 120 series, and the range recorder made it into the best ASW system. Lack of depth measurement was a serious drawback, not fully appreciated because of the shallow water in the main exercise area. RN submarines seem to have made little use of deep diving, so there was little input to doctrine from them. The lack of depth data combined with the time for a stern-dropped depth charge to fall to give a long dead time in which the U-boat could evade the attack. Failure to develop an ahead-firing weapon was the greatest failure of the pre-war Admiralty.

The possibility of night surface attack was appreciated and exercises had been carried out.[4] However, until the introduction of radar, detection of a surfaced submarine was visual and, on a dark night, the range of detection was short. Numerous escorts were the only, partial solution.

Wartime Developments

Wartime developments were largely correct and timely. The Flowers were entering service from mid-summer 1940 and large numbers were on order. The Tobermory training facility would put the finishing touch to the skills of the new crews. There were fifty ex-USN destroyers coming along, although it was some time before it was realised how much work was needed to make them operational. The design of a true ocean escort, the River class, only began in November 1940 but one has to excuse this late start as the Admiralty had many things on their minds during that wild summer of 1940.

The rapid development and introduction of radar and later improvements was a success, as were the ahead-throwing weapons and their associated depth-finding asdic. It has been suggested that some of these were introduced too quickly and that a longer development time would have meant that the first sets at sea were

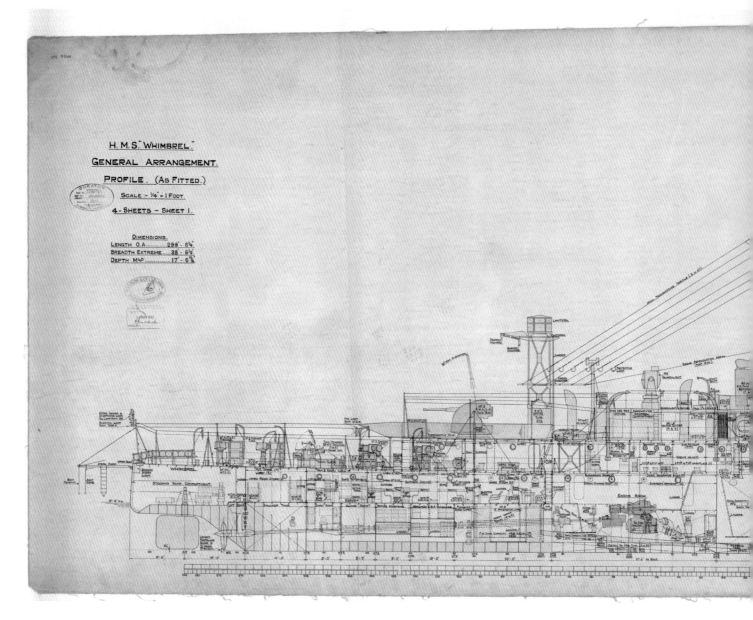

more reliable. There is some truth in this but getting the Mk I to sea quickly was an advantage in itself and almost certainly the quickest route to a fully capable and reliable Mk II.

In the earlier years, both sides had successes in intercepting and reading the enemy's coded signals, with the advantage swinging back and forth. Both sides were slow to realise that their messages were being read; indeed the Germans never did accept this possibility. The advantage finally settled with the Allies – Poland making valuable contributions – with heroic rescue operations, the development of shipborne HF/DF and the use of primitive computers that could read Enigma reliably and usually quickly.

How Good Were They?

The efficiency of an A/S system depends on the performance of the ship, the effectiveness of its sensors and weapons and on the skill of its crew. The economical use of manufacturing facilities is another part of the story. Finally, it must be re-emphasised that the object is the safe and timely arrival of cargoes.

Brown[5] and Collingwood[6] have attempted a partial answer by listing the number of U-boat kills credited to each class of A/S vessel. The crude statistics shown in table 10.1 differ slightly

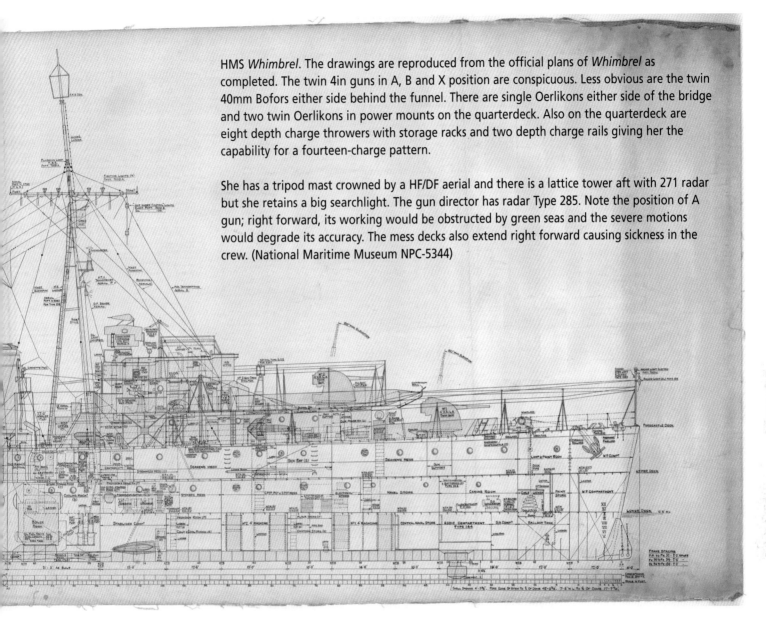

HMS *Whimbrel*. The drawings are reproduced from the official plans of *Whimbrel* as completed. The twin 4in guns in A, B and X position are conspicuous. Less obvious are the twin 40mm Bofors either side behind the funnel. There are single Oerlikons either side of the bridge and two twin Oerlikons in power mounts on the quarterdeck. Also on the quarterdeck are eight depth charge throwers with storage racks and two depth charge rails giving her the capability for a fourteen-charge pattern.

She has a tripod mast crowned by a HF/DF aerial and there is a lattice tower aft with 271 radar but she retains a big searchlight. The gun director has radar Type 285. Note the position of A gun; right forward, its working would be obstructed by green seas and the severe motions would degrade its accuracy. The mess decks also extend right forward causing sickness in the crew. (National Maritime Museum NPC-5344)

from those of Collingwood, probably as a result of different interpretations both of the boundary of the battle and of shared kills. The figures are very rough and ready, but they do suggest some interesting lines of thought, particularly when associated with the number of each category of escort at sea. In particular, the small number of *Black Swan*s scored a disproportionate number of kills. In seeking an explanation, it must be noted that the majority were scored by Walker's 2nd Escort Group.[7] The reasons for this start with the skill and determination of Walker himself (chapter 5); in turn, this led to the 'halo' effect, by which if a concentration of U-boats was located, Walker's group would be called up. There are indications that the best officers and most skilled ratings were chosen for the group. For a brief period, they were able to operate in the Bay of Biscay, working with aircraft against U-boats in transit on the surface, thanks to their heavy AA armament. The success of the group is the more remarkable in that few had Hedgehog and, until late on, none had Squid. In fact, one may query the value of the *Black Swan*s. At £360,000, they were 50 per cent more expensive than a River; they used more skilled labour, while their geared turbines gave little advantage over a River.

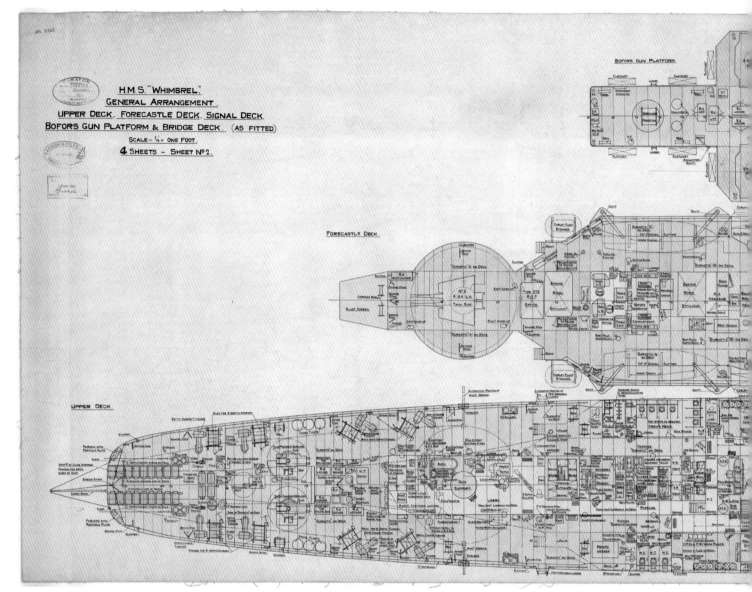

H.M.S. "WHIMBREL".
GENERAL ARRANGEMENT.
UPPER DECK, FORECASTLE DECK, SIGNAL DECK,
BOFORS GUN PLATFORM & BRIDGE DECK. (AS FITTED)
SCALE :- ¼ = ONE FOOT.
4 SHEETS - SHEET Nº 2.

BOFORS GUN PLATFORM

FORECASTLE DECK.

UPPER DECK.

Table 10.1: U-boat sinkings by class in the North Atlantic

Destroyers	
Modern	9
Inter-war A–I	39
Older (World War I)	26
Towns	8
Hunt	8
Sloops	
Black Swan	28
Older sloops	12

Table 10.1: *continued*

Frigates	
River	22
Loch	12
Captain	28
Colony	5
Corvettes	
Flower	38
Castle	5

The much greater success rate of the turbine Captains compared with the diesel ships has already been noted. Another interesting comparison is between the Flowers and the Rivers. They had the same asdic and depth

whimbrel has two boiler rooms and a single engine room giving some subdivision. Note the fin stabiliser under the bridge. The *Black Swans* were the Rolls Royces of the Atlantic but did their heavy gun armament and turbine machinery make them more effective ASW ships? (National Maritime Museum NPC-5345)

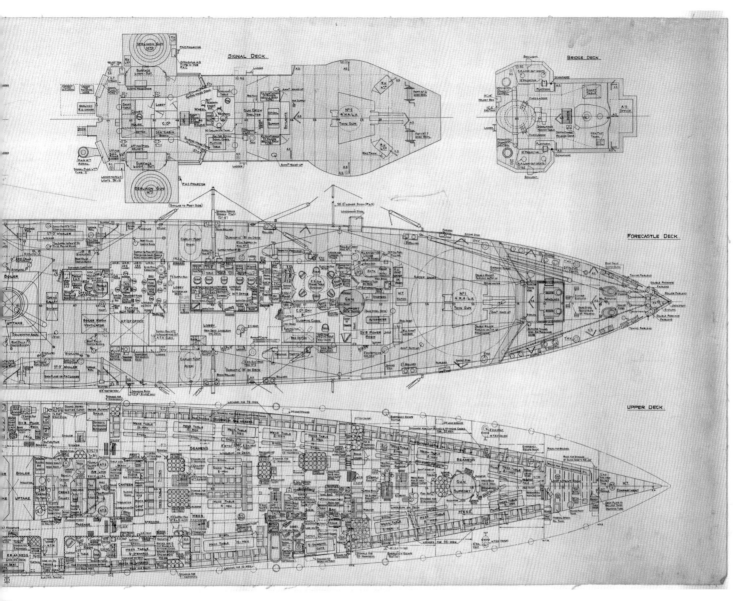

charge armament, both receiving Hedgehog as available. The Rivers were faster but used two engines, a bottleneck in escort-building.

The Rivers were much more successful 'killers' than the Flowers but they used twice as many scarce resources without scoring twice as many kills. Collingwood's more detailed analysis with months in commission per sinking gives 119.6 for the Flowers and 79.7 for the Rivers, a

broadly similar conclusion. Both analyses use sinkings as a measure of effectiveness, which grossly underestimates the value of the Flowers, because with early, short-range asdics, two sets are better than one. Two ships are also more effective than one in keeping submarines submerged, limiting their mobility. One may conclude that in the early years of the war the Admiralty, at least, were correct in building the

Table 10.2: Flower/River successes						
Year	1940	1941	1942	1943	1944	1945
Average no. in Atlantic	18/0	50/0	74/8	65/17	47/20	31/19
Kills	1/0	7/0	6/1	16/7	2/5	1/1
Kills per ship	–	14/0	8/12	25/41	4/25	3/5

simpler, single-engined ships.

There are insufficient data to make a similar comparison between the Castles and the Lochs but some conclusions may be drawn. The Lochs' double Squid was very much better than the Castles' single, but the weapons depended on the same asdic and operational plotting equipment and hence the cost difference between a Loch and a Castle was much less than that between a Flower and a River. Based on limited data, the kill rate for the double Squid was 40 per cent compared with 23.5 per cent for the single.

Figures for the installed electrical power (see table 9.4) also reflect the lesser difference in complexity between Castle and Loch. The continued building of the Castles was fully justified as they could be built on slips too short for Lochs.

With hindsight, one may debate the value of the Towns. They required a great deal of dockyard work to make them operational in ASW. They did not enter service until spring 1941, by which date Flowers were completing in some numbers. Once in service they needed frequent maintenance and repair. They sank a fairly small number of U-boats before their early relegation to subsidiary duties. On the other hand, their appearance in some numbers implied some support from the USA and was a valuable morale booster.

Summing Up

In 1939–40, the overwhelming need was for numbers. Numerous escorts with their short-range asdics were needed to prevent submerged attack. The only sensor against surface attack at night was the eyeball Mk I. The only way to get numbers quickly was to build Flowers, short enough to fit many available slipways and driven by simple reciprocating engines.

Later, with a sufficiency of escorts, the coming of asdic Types 144 and 147, together with centimetric radar, reduced the need for numbers, and Hedgehog and Squid made a lethal combination against the older generation of U-boats. However, the future lay with aircraft.

Tailpiece. The Egyptian *Tariq*, formerly HMS *Whimbrel* of Walker's escort group. At the time of writing (2007) it is hoped to bring her to Liverpool as a Battle of the Atlantic memorial.

Postscript
The Fast Submarine

This book is a history of escort vessels, not of U-boats, but some mention must be made of the German efforts to bring fast submarines into the Battle of the Atlantic. None of these newer boats was operational in the battle but it is worth considering what might have happened.[1] The development is a fine example of the adage, 'Requirements pull, technology pushes.'

The initial push came from Professor Hellmuth Walter, who, from about 1933, put forward a number of proposals for fast submarines using very concentrated hydrogen peroxide as the oxidant for the burning of fuel oil while submerged. This combination could be used either in a diesel engine, recycling the exhaust gases, or in a turbine. Walter wanted peroxide with a concentration of 80 per cent, when the strongest solution available was 45 per cent. This problem was overcome and in 1939–40 the experimental boat V80 was built. It had a submerged speed of twenty-eight knots on trials in 1940, demonstrating the potential of the scheme.

Four larger prototypes were built in 1942, two by Germania and two by Blohm & Voss. They were of 260–300 tons submerged and had most features of an operational submarine, achieving speeds of up to twenty-four knots. It had not been appreciated how much of the total drag of a submerged submarine was due to appendages such as open bridge, misaligned hydroplanes, even freeing ports. A small series of Type XVII boats was started, with a submerged speed of twenty-five knots, but none became operational. (U-1407 became HMS *Meteorite*

after the war.)

There were many problems still to be overcome, not least the in-fighting within the bureaucracy of the Third Reich and the more rational arguments of those who feared the delay to the building of conventional U-boats. However, by late 1942 a design had been completed for an operational 'Atlantic' U-boat, the Type XVIII. It was of 1,652 tons, with a design speed of twenty-four knots submerged and an endurance of 200 miles at that speed. Two were ordered in January 1943 but they were stopped in March 1944. There were other designs to follow but little had been done when the war ended. High Test Peroxide (HTP) is a very nasty substance, causing fire or explosion when in contact with many apparently innocuous materials. RN experience after the war, first with the ex-German *Meteorite* and later with the two British-built *Explorer*s, suggested that this was not the way to go.

Concerned with the delays in the Walter boats, the design office proposed to use the slippery shape of the Type XVIII for a fast battery boat, which was to become the Type XXI. There was to be a double pressure hull in a figure-of-eight configuration. The lower hull was to hold an enormous battery, three times the size of the older conventional U-boats. There were motors delivering 4,200hp to give a hoped-for seventeen knots. There were smaller motors for quiet running. Submerged displacement was 1,819 tons.

An elaborate production scheme was devised with nine hull sections built and fitted out in many factories and brought together for rapid assembly in a shipyard. Some thirty-two firms built structural sections; these were passed to one of sixteen specialist companies, which would install main and auxiliary machinery, piping, etc. In most cases, the sections were transported by canal. Finally, one of three building yards would put the sections together and carry out acceptance tests. Difficulties soon became apparent; labour of any sort was scarce and skilled labour very much so. In consequence, it was found that sections did not align correctly and installation was difficult, among many additional problems. After the war, a joint team from the rival British builders of the A class, Vickers and Chatham Dockyard, thought that both their prefabrication schemes were superior to that in Germany. The Type XXI was the first

U-boat with a complete hydraulic main (telemotor system) but it was poorly designed and bad workmanship led to many leaks. Since the system was mainly outside the boat, seawater contamination was common. There was also the Type XXIII, a small, fast conventional U-boat, but it played no part in the battle.

The design of the Type XXI's pressure hull was intended to provide a collapse depth of 330 metres, which allowed for an operational depth of 135 metres and a test depth of 200 metres. The design methods of the day could not really cope with the novel section shape and it was recognised that there were problems. Several attempts at a test dive had to be abandoned but on 8 May 1945, U-2529 finally reached 220 metres.[2] A post-war British study suggested 500 feet as a usable depth for the Type XXI.[3]

The next generation – *U2502*, a Type XXI with a smaller Type XXIII alongside. They would have been a formidable threat but unreliability delayed their entry into service.

For all its faults, the production system delivered 120 boats in two years but, mainly because of teething troubles, only one set out on an operational cruise, aborted when the war ended. Surface speed was about fifteen knots but, in other than a flat calm, the bridge flooded at speed. They were designed for rapid diving of twenty seconds and to achieve this a very large number of freeing ports were fitted. It was found that, submerged, these added 28 per cent to the drag of the boat. A practical submerged speed for an hour was sixteen and a half knots. Using the schnorkel, ten knots was obtained on trial but eddy shedding from the mast and periscope caused such severe vibration that the usable speed was about six knots. The quiet speed on auxiliary drive was also six knots.

They would have been formidable opponents but would not have had it all their own way. The essence of the convoy system was that it forced the attacker to come to the convoy, where the escort force was concentrated. Once the submarine was contacted, the Squid and its asdic would still be lethal, and the more capable Limbo anti-submarine mortar was only just round the corner. The Lochs would have retained some capability, as would the Captains if rearmed with Squid.

On the air side, early sonobuoys and MAD (magnetic-anomaly detection) were already in use before the war's end. Together with the Mk 24 'mine' they would have been a formidable counter to the Type XXI. Perhaps even more portentously for the future of anti-submarine warfare, helicopters were already flying. The development of all these technologies would have been rapid.

Appendix I
Diving Depth and Pressure Hull Strength

The ability of U-boats to dive to extreme depths came as a surprise to the RN and considerably reduced the effectiveness of the asdic/depth charge system as a result of the longer 'dead time'. In consequence, it is worth while giving some consideration to the realistic operational diving depth of German submarines.

There are three main ways in which the pressure hull of a submarine may fail as a result of sea pressure:[1]

overall collapse, in which a whole compartment collapses because of instability associated with inadequate frames;

interframe buckling, in which the plating between frames buckles in a large number of nodes round the circumference; this is not normally caused by static pressure but could be excited by a depth charge explosion;

yielding of the plating between frames.

There is a degree of approximation in the calculation of all these modes and in their application to real submarine operation. A considerable factor of safety is then applied to the calculated collapse depth to allow for errors including:

depth excursions; a small loss of control can lead to disaster if the submarine is deep;

errors in building, eg failure to maintain circularity, defects in the steel or in welding;

errors in calculation, either in the theory or in the execution of the design.

This leads to three depths governing the operation of submarines: collapse depth (whose meaning is all too clear), operational depth (with a big factor of safety) and test depth (it was normal to test at least one of each class to a depth greater than the operational depth).

During the 1930s, British designers could only calculate the case of plating yield between frames; the frame size was based on experience and was, understandably, cautious (ie heavy).[2] German theoretical work on pressure loading of stiffened cylinders led to an accurate method of designing frames, so that they could use much lighter frames with confidence. British designers inspecting U-570 after she surrendered were amazed by the small frames.[3] The weight saved in the lighter frames went into thicker plating, while the U-boats also gained from welding (probably worth another 50 feet of depth) and slightly stronger steel (yield strength of 22 tons/in^2; cf British S-quality steel, 18.5 tons/in^2). Initially, the Germans adopted a very cautious factor of safety, of about three. With experience and knowledge of the value of deep diving, this was relaxed.

Table A.1: Some figures for the Type VIIC U-boat

Pressure hull radius (R)	15.4 feet
Plating thickness (t)	0.728 inches
Yield strength (s)	22.9 tons/in^2

British plating strength was calculated using the 'boiler formula', which was surprisingly accurate:

pressure (depth) = s.t/R (in consistent units)

This gives the plating collapse depth for the Type VIIC as 1,033 feet. Rössler, quoting von Sanden/Gunther, gives 820 feet.[4] The official operational depth was 100 metres, consistent with a factor of safety of three. The figure for interframe buckling was similar to the plating collapse depth, while that for frame collapse was some 20 per cent greater. Rössler gives the greatest recorded depth as 876 feet, by U-331 (she was lucky). The Type VIIC-41 had thicker plating and a diving depth of 120 metres. Figures for the Type IX were similar.

Appendix II
Fitting of 6pdr guns

The following Flower class corvettes are listed in ADM 239/75 (formerly Admiralty confidential reference book CB 1815) as having a 6pdr in each bridge wing in April 1944 (photos exist of several): *Buttercup, Rose, Roselys, Eglantine, Stonecrop, Renoncule, Aconite, Narcissus, Lobelia, Campion, Vervain, Myosotis, Mignonette, Dianthus, Kingcup, Orchis, Kriezes (ex-Coreopsis – Compass Rose* in the film of *The Cruel Sea*), *Primrose, Nada* (ex-*Mallow*), HMCS *Brandon* (3pdr). Also the destroyers *Restigouche, Chaudière, Qu'appelle.* March adds: *Active, Anthony, Arrow, Antelope.*[1]

The gun was the Hotchkiss Mk I, dating from 1884, most on non-recoil mounts. It had a muzzle velocity of 1,765ft/sec, giving a range of 9,400 yards. HE and AP shot were available. No record of its use has been found.

Appendix III
Loss of Destroyers in Bad Weather

Brief details of nine losses from 1934 to 1944 follow.

Tomozuro, 16 March 1934, Japan. Capsized following heel due to beam winds combined with heavy rolling. Blamed on poor large-angle stability.[1]

Branlebas, 14 December 1940, France. Broke in half at break of forecastle in a moderate gale. Investigation of sisters showed very poor stability.

Lanciere, 23 March 1942, Italy. Progressive flooding through weak hatches, doors and superstructure caused loss of power followed by capsize.[2]

Scirocco, 23 March 1942, Italy. No details, probably as above.

Sokrushitelnyi, 22 November 1942, Soviet Union. Pooped, lost power and later broke in half.[3]

Warrington, 13 September 1944, USA. Flooded down intakes, lost power and foundered.

Hull, Monaghan and *Spence*, 18 December 1944, USA. These three ships were operating with a considerable heel resulting from a strong beam gale with heavy rolling superimposed. Water came down the boiler room intakes, shorting the switchboard and causing the vessels to lose steering. The ships capsized. The USN investigation blamed the CO's blind obedience of the Admiral's orders. It was not uncommon for RN destroyers to signal 'Cannot maintain course and speed' without any blame ensuing. The investigation also led to the 'Sarchin and Goldberg' stability standards, adopted in principle by many navies, including the RN.[4]

Appendix IV
Asdic Sets

In 1939, most destroyers had Type 128 asdic sets, sloops had Type 127 and trawlers Type 123, though there were probably a few older sets in use. Brief particulars of the more important sets follow. (For more detail see Hackmann.) Note that there were frequent updates to sets while in service; for example, the ultimate 128 was virtually identical to 144. These updates took place when the ship was in hand for other work. Information on ship-fitting is scarce and often unreliable. While this note was written with care, its complete accuracy cannot be guaranteed.

Type 121. Prototype tested in *Woolston* in 1931. Fitted in D, E, F and G class destroyers, some cruisers and the sloop *Enchantress*. First production retracting dome.

Type 123. Trawlers and other auxiliaries. Introduced 1934, replacing earlier Type 122. Detachable dome.

Type 124. Updated 121. In 1934–7 fitted to C, H, J, K and Tribal class destroyers, coastal sloops and a few older destroyers. First with standard range recorder.

Type 127. Designed for sloops but very widely fitted from 1937 in older destroyers, frigates and in allied ships. Dome as 122 and electronics as 123. Some had Q (qv).

Type 128. From 1937 in destroyers; prototype in *Acheron*, then A (retro-fit), L and Hunt classes. Dome and directing gear as 121, electronics as 127. There were at least nineteen wartime variants, with improved recorders, helmsman display, etc. Type 128 XE became 144. Some had Q attachment.

Type 141. US set QCJ/QCL found in forty-seven flush-deck destroyers, fitted with RN range and bearing recorder. It had no dome and a few were given British domes as Type 141A.

Type 144. Started May 1941. Introduced in 1942 into destroyers and major escorts after trials in *Kingfisher*. It was the first set specifically intended for ahead-throwing weapons such as Hedgehog. It was a complete redesign, although many of its features were worked into later updates of 127/128.

Type 145 was similar to 144 but had portable, rather than retractable, dome for slower escorts.

Type 147. Sea trials in *Ambuscade* in May 1943. Very much part of a weapon *system* – Squid. Depth measurement.

Q attachment. 1943. Wedge-shaped beam only 3° wide in horizontal plane. Could measure depths 300–700 feet. Fitted to Types 127 and 145 without the need for docking the ship; vessels with Types 128 and 144 needed docking. Fitting took two to six days. Production from April 1943. In an attack, the ship would switch to Q at about 1,500 yards.

Hadleigh Castle was the first ship with the complete system of 144Q, 147B and Squid (single). She visited the USA in September 1943, creating a major impression. The USN received forty sets from the UK and a further forty-five from Canada.

Notes and References

Introduction
1. V E Tarrant, *The U-Boat Offensive 1914–1945*, London, 1989; John Terraine, *Business in Great Waters*, London, 1989

Chapter 1
1. Robert M Grant, *U-Boat Intelligence*, Archon Books, Hamden, USA, 1969 (reprint by Periscope Publishing, Penzance)
2. David K Brown, 'Defeat in the Atlantic', *Warship* (2002–3)
3. Richard Compton-Hall, *Submarine Warfare Monsters and Midgets*, Poole, 1985
4. George Franklin, *Britain's Anti-Submarine Capability 1919–1939*, London, 2003, p. 18
5. G C Peden, *British Rearmament and the Treasury*, Edinburgh, 1979
6. Franklin, *Britain's Anti-Submarine Capability*
7. PRO ADM 116/2607
8. David K Brown, 'Sir Rowland Baker, RCNC', *Warship* (1995); also Nicholas Monsarrat, *East Coast Corvette* and *Corvette Command*, London, 1943, 1944
9. Arnold Hague, *The Allied Convoy System 1939–45*, London, 2000
10. Adm Sir William James, *The Sky Was Always Blue*, London, 1951. James claims to have thought out his organisation in the bath.
11. Willem Hackmann, *Seek and Strike*, Basingstoke, 1994 (general technical reference for this book)
12. David K Brown, 'Defeat in the Atlantic', *Warship* (2002–3)
13. The meaning of ASDIC. The letters 'ASD' represent the initials of 'Anti-Submarine Detection', but 'IC' does not stand for 'Investigating Committee' as often stated. Hackmann and Franklin have both shown that the '-ic' here is the suffix meaning 'pertaining to'. To preserve secrecy about the nature of the equipment, the term 'ASDivite' was coined to refer to quartz. Asdic is now known as 'sonar'.
14. Hackmann, *Seek and Strike*, p. 135
15. Peter Gretton, *Convoy Escort Commander*, London, 1964; D A Rayner, *Escort*, London, 1955; Gretton was in command of *Sabre*, Rayner of *Shikari*
16. Operation Catherine was Churchill's proposed foray by the Royal Navy into the Baltic in 1940 to interrupt German seaborne trade. Churchill was eventually persuaded against the operation and it was cancelled
17. Rayner, *Escort*
18. A Raven and J Roberts, *V and W Class Destroyers*, London, 1979; A Preston, *V and W Class Destroyers*, London, 1971; these are both excellent books, dealing with these ships in both wars, and are very well illustrated
19. March suggests in *British Destroyers* that some of the last Ws had ungalvanised frames
20. Working in the Channel in February 1944, *Warwick* had her Hedgehog replaced by a 4in QF gun
21. In riveted construction, rivets were spaced closer in oil-tight (OT) work than in merely watertight (WT) (spacing was 4–4½ rivet diameters for OT, and 4½–5 diameters for WT). I suspect that this was ignored in the conversions
22. D K Brown, 'V & W Conversions', *Warship Supplement* (101), World Ship Society
23. Fuel tanks that, because of their position in the ship, were not considered suitable for that purpose in time of war were known as 'peace tanks'
24. A15039, Imperial War Museum
25. Arnold Hague, *Sloops 1926–36*, World Ship Society, 1993
26. David K Brown, 'Sir Rowland Baker', annex concerning Baker's views on pre-war sloops, p. 152
27. Older sloops fitted with Hedgehog by October 1945: *Stork, Fleetwood, Aberdeen, Deptford, Lowestoft, Wellington, Leith, Fowey, Folkestone, Scarborough, Hindustan* (ADM 239/75)
28. Hague, *Sloops*
29. Eberhard Rössler, *The U-boat*, London, 1981

Chapter 2
1. Arnold Hague, *The Allied Convoy System 1939–45*, London, 2000
2. Geoffrey Carter, 'She is not what she pretends to be – the

Special Service Squadron', *Warship World* (9/12)

3. G A Rotherham, *It's Really Quite Safe*, Belleville, Canada, 1960; Rotherham says (p. 123) that she was hit by one torpedo but other sources suggest two

4. John Terraine, *Business in Great Waters*, London, 1989, p. 247

5. John Campbell, *Naval Weapons of World War Two*, London, 1985

6. J S Cowie, *Mines, Minelayers and Minelaying*, Oxford, 1949

7. Even after lengthy repairs, *Belfast*'s keel is still bent

8. Willem Hackmann, *Seek and Strike*, Basingstoke, 1994

9. PRO ADM 229/20

10. PRO ADM 229/20

11. Adapted from a table in PRO ADM 229/20

12. Goodall diaries, 25 March 1939

13. She was requisitioned in August 1939

14. J H Harland, *Catchers and Corvettes*, Rotherfield, 1992

15. A W Watson, 'Corvettes and Frigates', *Transactions of the Institution of Naval Architects* (1947)

16. H T Lenton, *British and Empire Warships of the Second World War*, London, 1998

17. Thomas G Lynch, *Canada's Flowers*, Halifax, Nova Scotia, 1981

18. Goodall diaries, summary entry, 1940

19. Watson, 'Corvettes and Frigates'

20. John English, *Amazon to Ivanhoe*, World Ship Society, 1993

21. Vice Adm H G Bowen, USN, *Ships, Machinery and Mossbacks*, Princeton, 1934, appendix 17

22. D K Brown, 'Stability of RN Destroyers during World War II', *Warship Technology* (10), Royal Institution of Naval Architects

23. Hackmann, *Seek and Strike*

Chapter 3

1. Jean Kessler, 'U Boat Bases in the Bay of Biscay', *The Battle of the Atlantic 1939–1945*, London, 1994

2. Derek Howse, *Radar at Sea*, Basingstoke, 1993

3. Jürgen Rohwer, 'The Wireless War', *The Battle of the Atlantic 1939–1945*, London, 1994

4. Arnold Hague, *Convoy Rescue Ships*, World Ship Society, 1998

5. Richard Baker, *The Terror of Tobermory*, London, 1972

6. The figures for horsepower and speed are suspect. Group D, with much less power, cannot be so much faster than the others. Admiralty confidential reference book CB 1815 for October 1945 gives these figures for *Leeds* but the others are 24,000–25,000shp for thirty-five knots. I suspect these were as-built figures and the lower speeds quoted in table 3.2 for

groups A, B and C are the best possible in the war

7. Arnold Hague, *The Towns*, World Ship Society, 1988. Mainly a set of individual ship histories but with an excellent introduction covering their design features and changes. See p. 10 concerning leaks

8. Cdr A H Cherry, *Yankee RN*, London, 1951; the personal story of a New York stockbroker who joined the RN and served in HMS *Reading* (see chapter 11 for steering problems)

9. Willem Hackmann, *Seek and Strike*, Basingstoke, 1994

10. PRO ADM 225/24

11. D K Brown (ed), *The Design and Construction of British Warships 1939–1945*, London, 1996

12. Private letter from Mr R F Linsell, formerly Lt Cdr (E) in *Gorleston*. See D K Brown, *Nelson to Vanguard*, London, 2006, p. 132

Chapter 4

1. The survival of *Kearney* was attributed to her unit system of machinery – boiler/engine/boiler/engine – and was an important factor in the adoption of this system in the RN. See D K Brown, *Nelson to Vanguard*, London, 2006

2. U-110's commanding officer was Lempe, who sank the *Athenia*

3. John Terraine, in his book *Business in Great Waters* (London, 1989), refers to this period of the battle as 'False Dawn', contrasting with my 'Gleam of Light'. I consider that developments in radar, asdic, numbers and training of ships, together with increasing US support, justify my interpretation despite the dreadful losses of 1942

4. Derek Howse, *Radar at Sea*, Basingstoke, 1993

5. A waveguide is a device to guide electromagnetic waves along a defined path with the minimum of energy loss

6. W H Smith, Old Trafford

7. Donald Macintyre, *U-Boat Killer*, London, 1956

8. P G Redgment, 'High Frequency Direction Finding in the RN', *Journal of Naval Science* (8/1)

9. Arnold Hague, *Convoy Rescue Ships*, World Ship Society, 1998, pp. 11 and 18; see also Jürgen Rohwer, *The Critical Convoy Battles of March 1943*, London, 1977, p.19

10. Howse, *Radar at Sea*

11. Rohwer, *Critical Convoy Battles*

12. Rohwer, *Critical Convoy Battles*, photos opposite p. 193

13. PRO ADM 225/24

14. *Deveron*, *Mourne* and *Tweedie*

15. A W Watson, 'Corvettes and Frigates', *Transactions of the Institution of Naval Architects* (1946)

Chapter 5

1. The Type X U-boat was designed as a minelayer: 1,763

tons surface; endurance 18,450 miles at 10 knots

2. Rowland Baker in a personal letter to the author; original in National Maritime Museum RCNC file

3. Goodall diaries

4. Arnold Hague, *Sloops 1926–1946*, World Ship Society, 1993

5. PRO ADM 234/76 in CB 1815 gives the following as fitted with Hedgehog by October 1945: *Black Swan, Erne, Sutlej, Flamingo* and *Stork*

6. Admiralty confidential reference book CB 1815 gives none by April 1944 and the following by October 1945: *Amethyst, Hart, Magpie* and *Pheasant*

7. D E G Wemyss, *Relentless Pursuit*, London, 1955

Chapter 6

1. Much of this chapter depends heavily on: Peter Gretton, *Crisis Convoy*, London, 1974; Jürgen Rohwer, *The Critical Convoy Battles of March 1943*, London, 1977; Jürgen Rohwer and G Hummelchen, *Chronology of the War at Sea 1939–1945*, London, 1992; S W Roskill, *The War at Sea*, vol II, London, 1956

2. *Pink, Alisma, Snowflake* and *Loosestrife*

3. *Inglefield, Eclipse, Fury* and *Icarus* (one hour later). *Fury's* asdic dome had been lost in bad weather. *Icarus* lost hers later

4. On the first run, the charges failed to drop. Manoeuvring the big aircraft under low cloud was difficult.

5. *Offa, Obedient, Orwell* and *Onslaught* joined *Oribi*

6. David K Brown, 'Stability of RN Destroyers during World War II', *Warship Technology* (4/1989), Royal Institution of Naval Architects

7. 'Canso' was the nickname for the Canadian-built version of the famous American Consolidated PBY Catalina flying boat

8. David K Brown and Phillip Pugh, 'Ramming', *Warship* (1990)

9. 'Deadlight' was the British operation to dispose of surrendered U-boats after the war, by scuttling or otherwise sinking them. See David Miller, 'Operation Deadlight', *Warship 1997–8*

10. Peter Hodges, *Royal Navy Warship Camouflage*, London, 1973; David Williams. *Naval Camouflage 1914–1945*, London, 2001

11. CAFO 679

12. Norman Friedman, *U S Destroyers*, Annapolis, 1982

13. Bruce Franklin, *The Buckley Class Destroyer Escorts*, Annapolis, 1999

14. Peter Elliott, *American Destroyer Escorts of World War 2*, London, 1974

15. C E Preston, *Power for the Fleet*, Eton, 1982

16. D K Brown, 'Atlantic Escorts 1939–1945', *The Battle of the Atlantic 1939–1945*, London, 1994

17. D J Collingwood, 'WW II Anti-Submarine Vessels', *Warship World* (summer 1997), Liskeard

18. Capt Donald Macintyre, *U-Boat Killer*, London, 1956

19. R E Johnson, 'The Tacoma Class Frigates of World War II', *Warship International* (2/82)

20. Nicholas Monsarrat, *HM Frigate*, London, 1946

21. Johnson, 'Tacoma Class Frigates'

22. Monsarrat, *HM Frigate*

Chapter 7

1. *St Croix, Polyanthus* and *Itchen* sunk; *Lagan* damaged.

2. John F White, *U-Boat Tankers 1941–1945*, Shrewsbury, 1998

3. Eberhard Rössler, *The U-Boat*, London, 1981

4. Rössler, *The U-Boat*

5. John Campbell, *Naval Weapons of World War Two*, London, 1985

6. Willem Hackmann, *Seek and Strike*, Basingstoke, 1994, p. 271

7. Goodall diaries

8. Bob Whinney, *The U-Boat Peril*, London, 1986

9. 'Watson is a really good man' (Goodall diary, 18 June 1940)

10. Loch class cover, note by Goodall, 30 October 1942. (The cover was a record of the design and construction of each class of ship. These invaluable documents are now held by the National Maritime Museum.)

11. Goodall diaries, 7 May 1943

12. Goodall diaries, 23 February 1944

13. A W Watson, 'Corvettes and Frigates', *Transactions of the Institution of Naval Architects* (1947)

14. Watson, 'Corvettes and Frigates'; discussion by Adams, *Transactions of the Institution of Naval Architects* (1947)

15. Watson, 'Corvettes and Frigates', discussion by C J W Hopkins, *Transactions of the Institution of Naval Architects* (1947), p. 179

16. Here and in the next paragraph, the numerous references to the Goodall diaries are identified by the date in the main text

17. D A Rayner, *Escort*, London, 1955; note also his description of the sinking of U-1200 by *Launceston Castle* with one salvo from her Squid (p. 226)

Chapter 8

1. The Mk 7 'Heavy' added to this problem.

2. Paint *is* surprisingly heavy; forty-five tons was removed

from the outside of a *Leander* after ten years in sevice

3. For example, Peter Gretton, *Convoy Escort Commander*, London, 1964. Gretton commanded HMS *Duncan*

4. D K Brown, 'Stability of RN Destroyers during World War II', *Warship Technology* (10), Royal Institution of Naval Architects

5. Letter from Sir Peter Gretton

6. Goodall diaries, 22 June 1941

7. D K Brown and P D Marshall, 'Small Warships in the RN and the Fishery Protection Task', *RINA Warship Symposium*, London, 1978

8. D K Brown, 'Atlantic Escorts 1939–45', *The Battle of the Atlantic 1939–1945*, London, 1994

9. This author would claim to be just about average in susceptibility

10. After the war, with more emphasis on speed in rough seas, the guideline became $1.3 \times \sqrt{(length)}$

11. A W Watson, 'Corvettes and Frigates', *Transactions of the Institution of Naval Architects* (1947), London; 'They would roll on wet grass' (Monsarrat)

12. Unreferenced quotations are from the ship's cover, held in the National Maritime Museum

13. K Monk, 'A Warship Roll Criterion', *Transactions of the Royal Institution of Naval Architects* (1987), London

14. James B Lamb, *The Corvette Navy*, London, 1979

15. J P W Mallalieu, *Very Ordinary Seaman*, London, 1944; Nicholas Monsarrat, *The Cruel Sea*, London, 1951

16. Report of the Talbot Committee

17. D K Brown, 'Atlantic Escorts 1939–45', *The Battle of the Atlantic 1939–1945*, London, 1994

Chapter 9

1. Goodall diaries, 2 June 1942

2. Ian L Buxton, *Warship Building and Repair During the Second World War*, Centre for Business History in Scotland, Glasgow, 1997

3. Ian L Buxton, 'British Warship Building and Repair', *The Battle of the Atlantic 1939–1945*, London, 1994

4. Matt McCarton, *Emergency Production Historical Study*, NAVSEA 05D-134-dtd. Nov 19, 2004, Naval Sea Systems Command, Washington DC, per P Sims

5. *History of the British Admiralty Technical Mission*, National Archives of Canada, RG 28, vol 29, per I L Buxton

6. Cdre (now Rear Adm) James Goldrick, email of 19 March 2005. He also comments that the fictional Australians in Monsarrat's *The Cruel Sea* are both very closely based on real men and have been identified

Chapter 10

1. G Franklin, *Britain's Anti-Submarine Capability 1919–1939*, London, 2003

2. Realistic convoy exercises are very expensive as they involve chartering merchant ships

3. G C Peden, *British Rearmament and the Treasury*, Edinburgh, 1979

4. Franklin, *Britain's Anti-Submarine Capability*

5. D K Brown, 'Atlantic Escorts 1939–1945', *The Battle of the Atlantic 1939–1945*, London, 1994

6. D J Collingwood, 'WW II Anti-Submarine Vessels', *Warship World* (summer 1997), Liskeard

7. The 2nd Escort Group destroyed twenty-three U-boats, of which nineteen were sunk by *Black Swan*s

Postscript

1. Eberhard Rössler, *The U-Boat*, London, 1981

2. Rössler, *The U-Boat*

3. J F Starks, 'German U-Boat Design and Production', *Transactions of the Institution of Naval Architects* (1948), London

Appendix I

1. David K Brown, 'The Technology of Submarine Design', *Interdisciplinary Sciences Reviews* (September 1990, vol 15/3)

2. David K Brown, 'Submarine Pressure Hull Design and Diving Depth between the Wars', *Warship International* (3/87), p. 279

3. Goodall diaries

4. Personal letter from Eberhard Rössler, September 1993

Appendix II

1. Edgar J March, *British Destroyers*, London, 1966

Appendix III

1. E Lacroix and L Wells, *Japanese Cruisers of the Pacific War*, London, 1997, p. 719

2. Amiraglio di Squadra G Politri and D K Brown, 'The Loss of the Destroyer *Lanciere*', *Warship* (1994)

3. P Kemp, *Convoy*, London, 1993, p. 114

4. D K Brown, 'The Great Pacific Typhoon', *The Naval Architect* (September 1985); Capt C R Calhoun, *Typhoon: the Other Enemy*, Annapolis, 1981; T H Sarchin and L L Goldberg, 'Stability and Buoyancy Criteria for US Navy Surface Ships', *Transactions of the Society of Naval Architects and Marine Engineers* (1962)

Bibliography

The books listed below are all from my personal library.

General History

Franklin, G, *Britain's Anti-Submarine Capability 1919–1939*, London, 2003. Review of tactics, training and, above all, exercises between the wars. Upsets many long-held ideas. See also the article by the same author, 'Asdic's capabilities in the 1930s', *Mariner's Mirror* (84)

Gretton, P, *Crisis Convoy*, London, 1974

Howarth, S and Law, D (ed), *The Battle of the Atlantic 1939–1945*, London, 1994, Proceedings of the 50th Anniversary Conference (I was chairman of the organising committee). A much-neglected but excellent source, with papers on a wide range of topics by the relevant specialists

Macintyre, Donald, *The Battle of the Atlantic*, London, 1961

Rohwer, J and Hummelchen, G, *Chronology of the War at Sea 1939–1945*, London, 1992; excellent detail source

Rohwer, J, *The Critical Convoy Battles of March 1943*, London, 1977

Roskill, S W, *The War at Sea*, 4 vols, London, 1954–61; the official history – good but written before the Enigma story was released (though Roskill was aware of it)

Showell, Jak P M, *U Boat Command and the Battle of the Atlantic*, London, 1989

Tarrant, V E, *The U-Boat Offensive 1914–1945*, London, 1989; an excellent history of the two world wars. I have followed his chronological breakdown

Terraine, John, *Business in Great Waters*, London, 1989; another fine book, particularly good on the air side

Weapon Systems

Hackmann, W, *Seek and Strike*, London, 1984; almost the only work dealing with A/S weapon systems. Very comprehensive.

Hezlet, Arthur, *The Electron and Sea Power*, London, 1975

Howse, Derek, *Radar at Sea*, Basingstoke, 1993; the story of the development of radar in the Royal Navy, written on behalf of the Naval Radar Trust.

Ships – General

Brown, D K (ed), *The Design and Construction of British Warships 1939–1945*, London, 1996; the DNC official history

Buxton, Ian, *Big Gun Monitors*, London, 1978

Elliott, Peter, *Allied Escort Ships of World War II*, London, 1977

Elliott, Peter, *Destroyer Escorts of World War 2*, New Malden, 1974

Hague, Arnold, *Convoy Rescue Ships 1940–1945*, World Ship Society, Gravesend, 1998; almost the only book on a little-known subject

Hague, Arnold, *Sloops 1926–1946*, World Ship Society, Kendal, 1993

Lenton, H T, *British and Empire Warships of the Second World War*, London, 1998; the most comprehensive listing

Rössler, Eberhard, *The U-Boat*, London, 1981

Watson, A W, 'Corvettes and Frigates', *Transactions of the Institution of Naval Architects*, vol 89, London, 1947; text follows DNC above but discussion is most important

White, John F, *U-Boat Tankers 1941–1945*, Shrewsbury, 1998

Ships by Class

Dickens, Peter, *HMS Hesperus*, Windsor, 1922

English, John, *Amazon to Ivanhoe*, World Ship Society, Kendal, 1993

Hague, Arnold, *The Towns*, World Ship Society, Kendal, 1988

Lavery, Brian, *River Class Frigates and the Battle of the Atlantic*, Greenwich, 2006; as well as addressing the River class, provides material on general topics such as training and messing

Lynch, Thomas G, *Canada's Flowers*, Halifax, Nova Scotia, 1982

Preston, Anthony and Raven, Alan, *Flower Class Corvettes*, London, 1973

Preston, Anthony, *V & W Class Destroyers 1917–1945*. London, 1971

Raven, A and Roberts, J, *V & W Class Destroyers*, Man o'
War, London, 1971. This and Anthony Preston's are
both excellent books. The different approaches make
them complementary rather than rivals

Some Miscellaneous Topics

Buxton, Ian, *Warship Building and Repair during the Second
World War*, Glasgow, 1997

Collingwood, D J, 'WWII Anti-Submarine Vessels', *Warship
World* (summer 1997); statistics of sinkings by class.

Hague, Arnold, *The Allied Convoy System 1939–1945*,
London, 2000; vital to an understanding of the battle.

Hodges, Peter, *Royal Navy Warship Camouflage*, London,
1973

Kent, Barrie, *Signal!*, Clanfield, 1993

McCarton, M and Garzke, W, *Emergency Production
Historical Study*, Washington, 2004

Moore, George, *Building for Victory*, World Ship Society,
Gravesend

Williams, David, *Naval Camouflage 1914–1945*, London,
2001

Winton, John, *Ultra at Sea*, London, 1988

Personal Accounts, Mainly Autobiographies

Chalmers, W S, *Max Horton and the Western Approaches*,
London, 1954

Cherry, A H, *Yankee RN*, London, 1951

Gretton, Peter, *Convoy Escort Commander*, London, 1964

Lamb, James B, *The Corvette Navy*, London, 1979; Canada's
Flowers

Macintyre, Donald, *U-Boat Killer*, London, 1956

Monsarrat, Nicholas, *HM Corvette* and *HM Frigate*,
London, 1942, 1946. Also *The Cruel Sea*; though fiction,
it is closely based on fact and is the best account of life
at sea in the battle

Rayner, D A, *Escort*, London, 1955

Wemyss, D E G, *Relentless Pursuit*, London, 1955; the story
of Capt Johnny Walker

Whinney, Bob, *The U Boat Peril*, 1986

Index